To the War

TO

THE WAR

by *ROBERT EDSON LEE*

Illustrations by Lorence Bjorklund

ALFRED A. KNOPF · New York 1968

THIS IS A BORZOI BOOK
PUBLISHED BY ALFRED A. KNOPF, INC.

FIRST EDITION

Library of Congress Catalog Card Number: 68–12666

Lines from "The Dry Salvages" from Four Quartets by T. S. Eliot are reprinted by permission of Harcourt, Brace & World, Inc.

WHEN I BEGAN this book, it was meant to be a straight, factual history, so that I could say: *This* is the way World War II really was. I realize now how subjective and selective memory is: the act of recalling is a shaping, fictive act. When it came to writing about other people, the fictionalizing, distorting process took over completely. "Web" and "Shep" and "Captain A——" are not Web and Shep and Captain A——. I have seldom used real names and I have not written about specific people. My hope is that the fictional truth here is more significant than the historical truth, that it has meaning beyond the time and place of World War II. Otherwise, it has no meaning to my sons Marc and John, to whom I dedicate this book.

Contents

April 1943-
January 1945

DEPARTURE

~~~~~~~~~~~~~~~~~~~~~~~~~~

THERE ARE MILLIONS LIKE ME, middle-aged, with small pot bellies, impatient, with sudden violences and sullen withdrawals that harbor with slight smiles the memory of our youth. We are the physically unscathed, those millions who served in World War II but made no physical and little mental contact with an enemy. The truth is that we enjoyed the war and would go again. It is necessary now in middle age to go back to the war, not out of the guilt of survival but out of the need to know if we learned anything—and with the uneasy leering fear that in fact we learned nothing.

However, I can speak only for myself. My experiences in the war were so unexceptional that my sons do not trouble to question me about them, preferring the melodrama of television. My album of photographs they have leafed through only once. They have not asked to read my letters home, stacks of letters that I take out now in secret in the effort of recall. I remember my stern injunction to my mother to save them, for I thoroughly expected the letters to break off somewhere in the midst of life, that they would be my only memorial—but they are so superficial and so baldly literary I can use them only as the starting point for my mid-night visions, now that I try to stand outside myself and learn something from my journey to the war.

"Drop us a card when you get there and write a letter next Sunday. I don't care how busy you are. Write a letter every Sunday."

"They censor the mail, you know. I won't even be able to say where I am."

"Write anyway."

"Then save my letters . . ."

I hear them now and look back and down with sardonic amusement at a classic scene. My parents had brought me to the train station, and we were alone on the platform. It was the end of March, nearly five o'clock in the evening, but timeless. The powerhouse across the track chugged like a fast pulse, masking other sounds. But we would be able to hear the train sounding two miles out of town, then at the canning-factory crossing, then at the half-dozen street intersections before it reached the depot. It was not much of a train—a Diesel engine, a baggage car, and a passenger car— and it was the only train of the day. It was not much of a town ("They're gonna pave the road to the cemetery and call 'em Twin Cities"). It was Iowa, in the spring of 1943, and I was going that evening only as far as the midshipmen's school at Notre Dame, Indiana, but after that, God knew where.

Even Notre Dame was farther than I had ever been before. I had once hitchhiked to Colorado and walked alone up Pikes Peak, and once I had ridden a caboose on a freight train to Chicago, but these were the boundaries of my experience to that day. I had gone to college, to Ames, a hundred miles from home. There I had drifted unaccountably into architectural engineering, enamored by an early discovery of the work of Frank Lloyd Wright, though I had become somewhat disillusioned by difficult courses in bridge design and the strength of concrete. My real life had centered around the campus visitors: Lunt and Fontanne, Katharine Cornell, Ruth Draper, Dimitri Mitropoulos, Thomas Mann, Robert Frost, Bernard DeVoto, and Margaret Mead. I read at Joyce and Dostoyevsky and joined a literary club and worked my way up to being the editor of a little magazine in which I published the work of my friends. I fell in love every month. In my junior year I lived a detested life in a fraternity house. On the Sunday afternoon of December 7, 1941, I had locked myself in my room to listen in peace to the broadcast of the New York Philharmonic—only to have the Brahms symphony interrupted by the announcement of the attack on Pearl Harbor.

We didn't even know where Pearl Harbor was! I went from room to room, listening to the conversations, then dashing back to my own room to record them and save them for posterity. Here they are:

"How do we find out which are the Japs and which are the Chinks?"

"Those with the horn-rimmed glasses are the Japs."

"Those bastards, those goddam dirty bastards. If you were in Frisco you could go all over and rape all the Japs."

"Roosevelt's been asking for this a hell of a long time."

"I've been waiting for this for six years. Yeah, I'm going to war."

"Lord only knows I still have a chem test tomorrow."

"Those goddam Japs! I'd like to get in the infantry. Those goddam Japs are cross-eyed and couldn't see straight to fire."

"Maybe this is just a bunch of hooey to make us buy defense bonds."

"Those goddam profs won't even know there's a war."

"Those shits, those goddam dirty little shits."

I record exactly as it was the talk of ten young men, one of whom, as in a lottery, was killed in the war.

No one, as I remember, quit classes to enlist, but all of us went, sooner or later. To avoid the Army (and because my older sister had precipitately married an ensign), I went to

Des Moines to enlist in a Navy program that would allow me to graduate before being ordered to active duty as an officer candidate. But I was turned down for bad eyesight and brought back only the image of a row of naked men in more assorted shapes and sizes than I could have imagined (one man had under his breastbone a cavity big enough to contain a fist; another wore a bag of herbs dangling from his neck—to ward off colds, he said). Undaunted, somewhat desperate, I chomped on raw carrots, as superstitious as anyone, rested my eyes, tried again, and was abruptly sworn in.

With the future irrevocable and graduation speeded up to March 1943, I began a short riotous senior year, taking with two friends a basement apartment with a fireplace. We held parties with whiskey—this on a campus where even beer drinking was cause for dismissal—and even faculty attended our parties. I was in love with a tall, willowy blonde. Shep's girl was in Iowa City; one memorable phone call cost him twenty-three dollars. Web was in love with my girl and with Beethoven. What fun we had! Conscious always of the approaching end. Web was an electrical engineer and went off to Washington to work on radar. Shep was a landscape architect and, the snob, went into the Air Corps to become a navigator. Graduation was a tragedy, and I had been home just eleven days when my orders arrived in the mail. "Proceed immediately," they began.

So there we stood, my parents and I, waiting for the little train to take me thirty miles to the junction with the main line east. We were so thoroughly self-conscious about the leavetaking that we hardly spoke except for their admonition to write and mine to save the letters. Although I had never been intimate with my father and was anxious to break the connection to my mother (the letters home became a new cord), when the train horn sounded in the distance I choked up like a kid. Later, from the train, I watched the beautiful Iowa hills in the sunset, all glistening from my uncontrollable tears.

NOTRE DAME

〰〰〰〰〰〰〰〰

THE CATEGORY V-7 (S) meant that after sixty days of intensive training on the Notre Dame campus we would become ensigns, not officers of the line but specialists, destined for additional training in aviation, ordnance, damage control, radar, or naval architecture. There were twelve hundred of us in the class; at intervals, to the terror of all, men were "bilged" to a total of one hundred; but the rest of us were made ready to go to war with an admirable speed and thoroughness. Thoreau described it: "The mass of men serve the state thus, not as men mainly, but as machines, with their bodies."

Reveille was at 0700. Calisthenics began four flights down and out in the yard at 0705. There was an indignity about being awakened at such an hour by the cry "All hands on deck," jockeying for a position at the urinals, and then throwing oneself downstairs half-dressed and out into the snow or rain or merely the chill to do push-ups and "burpies" and other impossible gyrations. Later in the day, every day, we drilled, marched, back and forth on the campus sidewalks or double-time on the track inside the stadium. We learned rifle drill with dummy rifles. We swam in the campus pool—dumped in with all our clothes on. We stood in formation before every meal, and on Saturday mornings marched in dress blues for Captain's Inspection. This we did even on the days we were vaccinated for small pox, tetanus, or yellow fever—ruthlessly jabbed by enlisted men so that our arms were paralyzed. The drills so thoroughly exhausted us that one troubled innocent asked right out in a class, "Sir, do they put alum in our eggs?" For we had all turned temporarily incapable of erections. The compensations were that we ate well and slept well. I suppose I have never since had such a sense of physical well-being or so respected my body. One elegant spring day our squad marched so precisely that the squad leader could abandon his chant, our heels hitting the sidewalk in a perfect autonomous cadence.

Meanwhile, we tried to master a new vocabulary. Beds became bunks; floors, decks. The right stairway became the starboard ladder and the left, the port (or do I still have them reversed?). Ropes turned into lines. The only gentlemen were officers. We sounded off, we mustered, we learned to use a ship's lead, to say nothing of the head. We spoke of Able, Baker, Cat, Dog. We *memorized* things like this: "A Pulling Life Boat is secured for sea if: Boat at davits, rigged out, griped against the strongback, gripes secured with a sea hook; falls clear, detaching hooks tended; steering oar in crutch; sea painter with a long lead forward and outboard of everything, brought aboard and toggled around the second thwart near the inboard gunwale." Not gunwale, but gun'l. And so on. Any ass can learn by rote, and it was not important that we had never seen the sea.

I quote a memorandum from the Ship's Company Officer to the Ship's Company; subject, haircuts: "The type of haircut to get is one with the clippers all around and high in the back with enough on top so it can be combed."

Then there were the trips to a hotel in South Bend where tailors' representatives waited in their rooms to oil us with cocktails while we were fitted for blues, khakis, and whites, "and a bridge coat, gentlemen?" The shoulder boards on the bridge coats made us swoon. God, we were elegant and pretty. We were clean, too, and I give the Navy credit for that, though I rather resented being put "on the tree" for a room inspection because a certain despicable senior officer ran his white-gloved finger across the *underside* of the plug to our wash basin.

All this struck me as rather childish, but I realize now that it was but accompaniment to the inculcation of unquestioning obedience. We were regaled with the story of an officer who spanked his young daughter if she did not say "Yes, *sir*." We were taught an absolute correctness, a propriety that might have some meaning on a ship in time of war; but we were, dammit, in Indiana, and there was no war in sight. While we lined up for inspection, the faculty-priests of Notre Dame watched us from across an invisible barrier. But how like them we were.

My future was fixed in an unbelievable manner, and I should have learned something about the nature of the universe from this, but I didn't. I was ordered down from the barracks to the administration building on the double. In absolute panic (*Have I been bilged?*), I presented myself to a certain senior officer whose name I didn't quite catch. He had had a letter from his daughter Gloria about me. (*Who?*) She had heard I was at Notre Dame. (*Which one was she?*) He had taken the trouble to look up my records and could say that I was doing fine work, just fine. Now, just which of the advanced courses would I like to attend? (*Was she the dumpy brunette on that picnic?*) Yes, I might just be fitted for the naval-architecture course at Ann Arbor. (*Was she that redhead in Econ?*) Anything else he could do, just let him know. (*Gloria who?*) That will be all.

My odyssey, my very life, hung on that five-minute interview, and I reel at the thought.

After sixty days at Notre Dame, I was dubbed an officer and a gentleman, but before going to Ann Arbor, I had to sit out another sixty days at the Great Lakes Naval Training Center north of Chicago. I did nothing there but grade officers' papers in a correspondence course in naval law. Great Lakes was boot camp to thousands upon thousands of enlisted men, learning, as I had, to be automatons. One day I had to return one hundred and seventeen salutes. Meanwhile, I lived with other officers in a palatial private home in Lake Forest. We were entertained at the Owentsia Club, and money fulfilled its patriotic duty by offering up its daughters in the belief that beneath the officers' uniforms there were indeed gentlemen. We had been well drilled; we acted like gentlemen, and that was that.

I was a gentleman, too, late in the summer when my college girl, the tall blonde, came to visit. She wore a white sheath of a dress, and I wore my white uniform, and we were young and in love. We went to Chicago to see Ruth Chatterton in *Private Lives* and then danced to Cab Calloway at the College Inn and still later walked out onto a breakwater and held each other tight. I came that close to proposing—but must have known just enough not to—and that was all. We never saw each other again.

ANN ARBOR

A PERSON GAINS, eventually, a certain respect for war because it is such a huge, consuming monster. It is not one malevolent person ("Who's in charge here?") but a way of thinking, common to all. It seemed to me then only a chaos; now I see it as some massive architectural order. Someone could think, was able to think, in terms of so many units of this, ten thousand of those, a million of that, the units constantly in motion. Someone ordered up two hundred submarines, a billion or so rounds of ammunition, and—the subtle shift of thinking impersonally—a thousand Chinese-speaking American soldiers, another thousand to speak Japanese, Russian, and (as an afterthought) a mere eighty hull-repair specialists for the Navy, and if we don't have them, we'll get them. Immediately.

The eighty hull-repair specialists were pulled from various universities or from ships at sea and quartered on the campus of the University of Michigan along with three thousand language-school soldiers and sixteen hundred V-12 trainees (who saluted us at every opportunity between

classes). The eighty of us began a course in naval architecture: four years of course work jammed into thirty weeks,
and the devil take the hindmost. The Navy's plan was to
turn out specialists in hull repair, knowledgeable in metallurgy, structural steel, and the intricacies of ship design to
the end that damaged ships could be quickly repaired and
put back into service. A Navy staff of four officers and six
yeomen would handle the administrative details, and the
university professors would handle the actual instruction.
It was a plan with a built-in structural fault.

The school of naval architecture at Michigan had in the
past supplied part of the very small demand for ship design-
ers in the United States; it was there primarily because of
the Great Lakes boat traffic and specialized in the design of
giant ore carriers. The small staff of professor-engineers was
inland-sea and nonmilitary and concerned primarily with
theory. Their work centered on the underground water
tank, some fifteen feet wide and four hundred feet long, in
which scale models of ships were tested for efficient design
(to an accuracy and scale, for example, of 1 to 30.409). It was
a tank so ancient the attendant boasted the green water had
not been changed since 1933. The university staff, so we
thought, was equally stale.

Was there a war on? We had first to review our college
algebra and calculus and then learn differential equations,
but this meant a one-year course in six weeks. We had a
course in microscope metallurgy, concerned with the effect
on molecular structure of the tempering of steel. Then,
given the dimensions of a certain ore carrier, we embarked
on six weeks of calculations—fascinating work—finding
drafts, displacements, metacentric heights, water lines, etc.,
figured on the basis of design lines laid out on a sheet of
paper six feet long. Twenty cross sections of the vessel had
to be drawn on the paper to an accuracy of $\frac{1}{192}$ inch or the
resulting calculations would be useless. Painstaking, marvelous work, had there not been a war on! Then we designed

the rivet spacing for a continuous girder that was the keel of a ship (rivets! when ninety-five per cent of the present ships built used welded joints), or we made a graphical expansion of data on the oscillations of a ship due to wave and wind combinations in order to arrive at certain constants to go into a nineteen-integer design formula. Classes every morning, labs every afternoon, homework every night, weekly exams in all subjects, and a weekend problem, say on the astern torque of a pan rudder, the calculations taking anywhere from four to twenty-four hours, depending on how long it took to find someone who had figured out the right answer. It was too demanding, too intense, too theoretical, too remote. We simply could not conceive of the need for such knowledge.

A crisis occurred one day when Professor A—— put on the blackboard a formula with forty-six integers in it and then boasted that it would take a fifteen-place logarithm table to solve it. Someone blurted out, "Sure, just get the log table from the library on Guadalcanal. What the *hell* are we doing this for?"

In a rage, Professor A—— reported this insult to the Navy commander, who immediately ordered us all to a lecture on manners and morale, concluding in all solemnity by saying, "Remember, gentlemen, every day, all you have to do is to say to yourself, 'This is the day I'm going to lick the Japs!' " It became our jeering theme song.

My letters home from Ann Arbor that bleak winter of 1943-4 were filled with bitching. I caught psychosomatic colds regularly in the mood of black despair. My grades slipped, I was warned, I was given a private pep talk—the same nonsense about licking the Japs—and I joined the crowd at the Pretzel Bell. Every university has the equivalent of the P. Bell: steamed-over windows, a brightly lit room, pitchers of beer, a bowl of hard-boiled eggs, and the lovely clatter of talk. My roommate and I would each drink a pitcher of beer and eat one egg; he pays who guesses most accurately the time the next girl takes getting in and out of the Ladies'.

Then we were taken in hand, six of us, by Professor A. E. R. Boak and his wife. Arthur Boak was a specialist in Roman history, a mild-mannered red-faced man, the very model of a professor with his austerely furnished living room, his littered basement study, his Irish setter, his pipes, and his garden. But to balance the obvious, he took a great interest in people; he was a man who listened more than he talked. Mrs. Boak had an organizing energy and a bubbling enthusiasm and just the right need for a son or several sons. She would collect our ration stamps and cajole her butcher into saving for her a standing rib roast; or she would order a small barrel of live lobsters from Maine and then phone for a bevy of sorority girls to join us for a feast. Soon, the six of us felt at home and were constantly underfoot, like puppies, time-consuming, demanding, and—I especially— turning to Mrs. Boak to pour out our troubles as to a surrogate mother. Well, I write this in lasting tribute to them both.

Meanwhile, I fell in love again. Given the war and my loneliness, it was predictable that I would go on weekends to Detroit and find in the USO Officers Club the greatest girl who ever lived—two such girls, in fact, one after the other. I use their real names, Lois and Maga, and send over the span of twenty years renewed affection. But the measure of the depth of our love is that the two girls are now indistinguishable in my memory. (Pity the man who married only because of the excitement of the war.) But even knowing now what I know about love, little as that may be, I know how transient and how lovely was our relationship, compounded of my uniform and the uncertain future and places like Cadillac Square and the Alibi Bar and the Ponchartrain Wine Cellars and the hard benches of the bus station where I sat out the early morning hours in perfect ecstasy, waiting alone for the five o'clock bus back to

Ann Arbor. Say only that we touched and went again into the night of the past.

In spite of these distractions, the paper war at Ann Arbor seemed endless. The first reports of grades went in to Washington with a list of forty-five out of eighty flunking the course. Word came back that hull-repair specialists were vital and to scale the grades upward to fit the need. Long shore leaves were to be granted, and field trips were scheduled as morale boosters, as exposure to reality.

So we went by ferry across Lake Michigan (my first ship!) to Manitowoc, Wisconsin, to watch the launching of a submarine. We went next to northern Michigan, to Bay City on Lake Huron, to watch the launching of a destroyer escort and the "rollover" of another—a fine example of Yankee ingenuity that deserves to be detailed.

The speed of ship construction depends on the available space at the launching ways, on the number of cranes available, and on the very slow work of placing and welding hundreds of sheets of plate steel on the hull. Someone at the Defoe yard at Bay City put these factors together and ordered the hull to be built upside down for easier, quicker welding; then the finished hull could be rolled upright onto the ship ways, as soon as the preceding ship had been launched. Thus, two ships under construction in the space and time of one.

A ship launching is always exciting, but especially so in a side launching. The ship is supported on a series of athwartship slanting timbers on the edge of the water—at Bay City a very narrow slip. On signal, the supports are knocked away and the ship, heeling to one side, slides into the water, coming to rest upright and waterborne. The U.S.S. *Raby*, with flags flying and band playing, was thus launched, sending a giant wave of water on the spectators across the slip.

Immediately, the next DE was made ready for the ways.

Two large circular supports had been placed around the upside-down hull; steel cables from two cranes were to be used to turn these enormous wheels. But consider. The hull was three hundred feet long and weighed seven hundred and fifty tons. The entire weight rested on the two wheels, putting stress on every welded joint of the hull. The stress was calculable, was, in fact, exactly like the situation of a ship resting on two wave crests in a storm, causing the ends of the ship to sag or "hog." Riveted joints under stress will slip enough to adjust and relieve such pressure, but welded joints do not slip, and steel is flexible only up to a point. In the change of stresses brought on by the slow rolling motion, there was the distinct possibility that the hull would tear apart. So the cranes pulled on the cables, and for three minutes this block-long mass of steel rotated, jerked, stopped, vibrated, and rotated some more, the bow in midair whipping back and forth noisily in the utter silence as thousands watched; and finally, with a groan, the hull settled upright on the ways.

It was really beautiful to watch, but we did not see the application to ourselves until Professor A—— lectured to us on the spot. "Remember, gentlemen, the planning that made this possible. No Jap or German could do it, because they would not *think* of doing it. *That's* how we are going to win the war, in drafting rooms, *just like ours.*"

Sobered, we drove back to Ann Arbor.

In midwinter, we spent six days touring factories in Detroit. There were *3,600* war plants and *2,000,000* workers in the Detroit area. Who can conceive of this? We watched steel made and rolled, orange-hot, into armor plate. We watched pontoons made, destined for unknown beachheads. We watched shell casings for 40mm. shells being stamped from disks of brass and shaped into nine-inch cylinders. We saw tubing drawn from brass, copper, and aluminum. We rode "water buffaloes," tanks, which clattered across fields, smacking down small trees, and then wallowed down into the Detroit River, miraculously floating. We saw bearing rods made for the engines of PT boats, the dimensions checked to an accuracy of 0.0002 inch. We watched breech blocks made, and gyroscopes (a worker braided wires finer than human hairs, twisting, waiting, twisting, a task so nerve-racking Sperry Gyroscope could hardly find in the entire country enough men who could stand such work) and blower fans and ship propellers and fuel injectors.

Consider only one operation in which a fifty-pound brass cylinder had to be fitted inside a steel cylinder. To ensure a tight fit, the brass was machined to a few thousandths of an inch *larger* in diameter than the steel cylinder and then frozen to $-40°$ temperature, shrinking in the cold just enough so that it could be slipped inside the steel cylinder. The brass cylinder would expand rapidly after it was removed from the freezer, and so the two workers had just ten seconds for their job. Every motion had to be precise. Pinchers were chilled, fitted onto the brass cylinder. The men looked at each other silently; one nodded; then they heaved. The frozen brass smoked in the warm air. Deftly it was slipped into the steel cylinder, tapped into alignment—all in less time than it takes to read about it—and the job finished, the workers stood there glossed with sweat.

We saw thousands of workers and we walked miles of factory, and at the end of the six days, we had seen only fifteen war plants out of the 3,600. The irony is that the tour, though designed to boost our morale, was used to boost the morale of the workers. We were treated in each plant like war heroes with welcoming speeches, refreshments, photographs; and we shook a thousand grimy hands and supposedly "inspired" the workers in some mysterious way. We were shamefaced not to be heroes, embarrassed that we had found our university work so onerous and meaningless. But we learned that much of the war was just that: onerous drudgery, seemingly endless and therefore meaningless—a design for a mountain of matériel, fantastically shaped, potent, deadly, and huge beyond any man's belief.

PORTSMOUTH

~~~~~~~~~~~~~~~~

IT IS STILL DARK at six when LeBlanc and I awake, not by an alarm clock, for we have been unable to buy one for love or money, but by force of will, by anxiety. We throw yesterday's newspaper into the fireplace (the mantel has the distinctive reeded carving of Bulfinch) and stand there smoking cigarettes and cursing our genial land-lady, Madame Paris, who has charged us so much for our apartment yet refuses to provide heat at such an early hour. We pad barefooted on icy linoleum and cook ourselves breakfast of sorts while taking turns in the bathroom and getting into Navy blues. We go down a circular staircase a hundred and fifty years old and take our yellow-painted Navy bicycles from the foyer and in the dawn (snow on the ground, robins singing wildly) emerge on Middle Street, never failing to be stunned by the eighteenth-century houses that were there when Washington and Franklin and John Paul Jones were there.

Between us and the Navy Yard (Yahd, it is called) is a line of stalled cars two miles long. LeBlanc and I mount our bicycles and thread in and out, past the Blue Goose restaurant (to wave at the waitress I'm dating), past the Athenaeum on Market Square, past the rotten docks at Strawberry Bank, and onto the bridge across the Piscataqua River (Pis-*cat*-a-quog, they say). We can see the Yard now and the monstrous black building, the Hill, where we work; and we can look down into the tidal river and see a lobsterman hauling in his lobster traps, surrounded by screaming gulls. We cross into Maine and down the street of Kittery to where the workers jam the gates to the Yard and then disperse to various buildings. LeBlanc and I go with some five hundred men and women into the largest of all, into the temporary and awesome silence just before the shift begins.

There is no hill to the Hill. One end of the building abuts the river (more bay than river); the tilt of the ways down to the river is barely twenty feet. But the Hill, the building, is some four hundred feet wide and six hundred feet long and ninety feet high, a chilling enclosed space. Entering at the center of the east side, we see to the right the preassembly areas where there are large segments of submarines, cylinders of yellow or dark-green steel; these are dwarfed by the crane space above, but they are large enough themselves to dwarf the welders who are putting on their leather jackets and pants. To the left, we see through the mazes of staging the bows of five (five!) submarines, jutting out and up, like so many meat cleavers or scimitars, and downhill, down the length of the building, the five squat bodies, larger by far than whales, waiting for their respective launching days when the glass wall on the river opens to let the subs slide into the river. The size of Detroit impressed me less than this, because it is here that I work (though only for five months) and here that I learn the very base of war.

We have arrived at the peak of submarine construction, when submarines are most needed in the Pacific; they make a force more significant than the Marines or the Army or the Air Force in the silent, steady destruction of Japan's naval

power. At Portsmouth, at Manitowoc, at New London, at
Mare Island, the submarine fleet is shaped, and each day is
vital, each hour. The strategy for rapid construction is the
prefabrication of segments of the hull, which can then be
lifted onto the ways, cutting as short as possible the close
work in the restricted area of the assembled hull. The work
on each submarine involves eight hundred separate work
orders, carefully timed to fit together into the space of some
one hundred prelaunch construction days. Like an intricate
stack of cards, one card misplaced and the whole stack tum-

bles down. And in fact there are cards, eight hundred of them for each submarine, in several keyed colors in racks in a building alongside the Hill; there fifty or so civilian foremen come each morning to pull out the jobs for the day; there a small task force of junior Navy officers (LeBlanc and I and six others) supervise the operation as troubleshooters, as referees between the various trades.

("Gahn damn it, they ain't finished cohkin' the enjin room on the *Robin* an' I got to git mah min in theh this mohnin' foh a preshah test an' until they git that equiptment aout, they ain't room to shee-ut.")

Late in the morning I go out to *my* boat, the *Sea Robin*, SS 407, but I am embarrassed to do so, for it is a routine policing of the boat, not for any specific job. Although I once break up a dice game, I never find the man who reputedly tends his own bar all day long, or the rumored prostitute who moves from one compartment to another. Rather, I am supposed to shame by my Naval Presence the men who would knock off for lunch an hour before lunch, or simply to check on compartment ventilation or safety or fire hazards—no small matter, for the yard fire trucks come roaring into the Hill on the average of once each working shift—or perhaps to summon the ambulance, to pick up some poor screaming creature who was momentarily careless with an acetylene torch and has put a quick deep hole in his thigh. Once a crane accidentally drops two tons of steel; the concrete floor is gouged out, luckily not a human being.

But now, to look at the Hill, there is no apparent humanity, only ants swarming over the bald, enormous bodies of the submarines. The noise is deafening, the air thick and green with welding smoke, the light now coming in great spasmodic flashes from welding or cutting torches. It is a hellish and seductive scene.

I speak (yell) to workmen I recognize, Jiggs, Mr. Brissom, others, and climb the long ramp up the side of the *Sea*

Robin. It takes half an hour to work my way through the sub; the men are corking the walls in the officers' quarters; one Diesel engine hangs suspended from the crane cables over the engine room and is nursed down into precise position. In the battery room, the rubber men are finishing the rubber lining on the floor. And so on—but it is time for me to inspect a tank.

("Lee, I know we're taking turns, but Smith wants this job done yet today, and I just don't have any choice. I'm sure sorry."

"I suppose it's a number-seven."

"Well, yes, it is, I guess."

"If you weren't so goddam fat—"

"I know, but, well, like the man said, you're the only one 'soople' enough to get in the thing.")

The actual working, functioning part of a submarine is the inner shell, a perfectly round cylinder, approximately fifteen feet in diameter; the outer shell is somewhat squat and heart-shaped, some twenty-five feet across in cross section, thus five feet out from the inner shell at the widest point. The enclosed space is made up into a series of tanks for fuel oil or fresh water or salt water (by filling or emptying the salt-water tanks, the submarine submerges or rises). The two hulls are tied together by steel frames spaced some two feet apart the length of the boat, and of course the two hulls merge into one at the narrow bow and stern. Near the stern is the narrowest tank of all, the number-seven, and before the tank is closed, ready for launching, somebody has to go inside with a flashlight and inspect the welding seams. Access holes are cut into the separating frames for this purpose, so that each bay of the tank can be reached. These holes are spaced horizontally two feet apart, and each hole is precisely twelve inches by sixteen inches—and sixteen inches is not a wide enough space to get both shoulders through at the same time. The inspector hangs in the closed space of the tank, supported only by inch-wide bands of steel at two-foot intervals, and, flashlight in hand, must pull himself, scrounge, from one bay to the next. The inspector, me.

It is my concept of hell. I lie there in pain, a cramp immobilizing me, in eerie cold darkness. Then some damn idiot with an air hammer begins chipping steel on the outside of the tank, an inch away from my head. The tank is my coffin. If I cannot move soon, the claustrophobia and the noise will drive me insane.

A moron dwarf could have done a better inspection job than I did, but each week I slithered down some fifteen or so tanks. I began to despair of ever "contributing to the war effort" in any satisfying sense, or of using the lengthy, expensive training at Ann Arbor for other than my own private education—and not one that I would have chosen voluntarily at that. Then Lieutenant Commander Smith, who supervised the troubleshooting operation, put me at a drafting table with a massive roll of blueprints and a magnificent problem.

Prelaunch construction could be speeded up as much as two days (at a saving of perhaps a million dollars) if two sections of the submarine could be fitted together outside the Hill and then brought in by a huge truck and lifted by the cranes onto the ways. The preassembled section would weigh 98,000 pounds. Two cranes together could pick it up, but the rated capacity of each crane was 40,000 pounds. The crane company advised that an overload of the cranes was possible for a maximum of ten minutes, provided each crane carried exactly half the 98,000 pounds. This could be ensured by the precise spacing of two lifting pads equidistant from the center of gravity of the section. Problem: find the combined center of gravity of three hundred shaped pieces of steel. An engineer or a mathematician will recognize that the problem, though tedious, was really very simple (not, however, the sort of thing a moron dwarf could do). At the end of five or six days of calculations, I had my answer. Much to my chagrin, I discovered that the lifting pads had already been welded on by the shipfitter foreman, who had simply taken his twenty years of experience and guessed— some six inches away from my calculation. Lieutenant Commander Smith spent an hour with my figures and then ordered the pads moved.

As a precaution, the first test of the cranes was made on the night shift when there were comparatively few people around to get hurt. A time was set, the crane company representatives arrived along with Smith, four or five other lieutenant commanders, the admiral of the Yard, and, to my horror, two ambulances. The section came in on the truck at a snail's pace, the multiple tires of the truck nearly squashed flat by the tremendous weight. The cranes drifted over through the welding haze and lowered their hooks, one picking up a worker to fit the hooks onto the pads. The worker climbed down off the section, and everybody backed away. Then the cranes took hold . . .

Of course it worked. "No sweat," as we said (sweating).

I had made my contribution. The Navy had gotten its money's worth out of me. I find, twenty years later, that I am nagged by never being able to know this *for sure:* without me, Smith might have found someone else who could do the calculation, or he might have relied on the guess of the shipfitter foreman. But I was and am reasonably convinced that the burden did indeed rest on me. It was to be the *only* time I did anything in the war by my standards worth *my* while.

Meanwhile, another submarine was ready for launching, the climactic event. The launching detail was organized out of our office, and I was given two tasks to perform. With some solemnity, Smith opened a locker in his office and selected a bottle of champagne (American) from a case (a case—such was the scale of our operation). With no little self-importance. I tucked the bottle under my arm and trotted across the Yard to the sail loft and delivered the bottle to the nineteenth century (I swear the man and his loft had sat there immobile since the days of clipper ships). Later, I received back the bottle encased in a mesh of string, decorated with red, white, and blue ribbons, and neatly attached to a lanyard; this I solemnly delivered back to Smith, who then carefully checked off that particular item from his long list.

My next task—but by then the workers had finished their last-minute jobs (the foremen riotous in our office), the ventilation and welding equipment had been removed from the submarine. Pennants were strung from the superstructure to the bow and the stern; bunting had been draped over the bow and the doors to the forward torpedo tubes in order to hide certain details from press cameras. The great window on the Piscataqua had been opened, and a gang of some hundred men had been stationed with sledge hammers on both sides of the boat. At 11:03, with one blast on the klaxon, each man delivered three blows on a wedge, and so on, at seven-minute intervals for six rallies, gradually transferring the weight of the submarine to a complex arrangement of dogshores and hydraulic jacks so that, at precisely 12:15, at the touch of a button, the submarine would drop onto the slanted greased ways and its own weight would slide it out of the building and into the river.

Workers began to gather, crowding onto the adjacent submarines and opening their lunch pails as if on a picnic. A Navy band appeared and began to play. At 11:50, the sponsor's party arrived. I could see them in the distance, uphill, for Lieutenant (j.g.) Gardner and I stood at the water's edge by the stern of the sub, one on each side, zipping on filthy coveralls. At 11:55, on signal, we began our ten-minute task: to move through the shoring the length of the boat for the

last inspection of the sliding ways. Although Smith had assured us that the launching would not go off until we had
reported personally to him that the ways were clear, there
was a certain anxiety about the delicately poised submarine
and the trigger mechanism, to say nothing about Smith himself. Was it possible that Smith might be so overwhelmed
by the dignitaries and the gold braid and the photographers
that he might forget us? And if we got stuck in the shoring?
Would Smith really sacrifice his precious schedule to ex-
tricate us? Each sliding way was some two feet wide, several
hundred feet long, black with grease. Most of the distance,
Gardner and I simply walked along, but at the cribs we
crawled and shoved, as in the restrictive area of the number-
seven tank. There, it seemed to take an hour to advance an
inch. Further, we noted that young Marines with subma-
chine guns stationed themselves in protective attitudes after
we passed, lest a saboteur toss a hammer onto the ways. Had
the Marines been told about us? But even before we reached
the bow, one long horrifying blast on the klaxon silenced
the Navy band and the spectators. Could they really, con-
ceivably launch the sub before we reported out? Just how
expendable to Smith were we? But here, Gardner crossed
over to me; we had finished. Smith dashed down the stairs
from the launching platform, searching for us. We had not
touched the grease on the ways, but we were black, perhaps
unrecognizable. Perhaps he wouldn't find us. We conferred
and decided to salute. We did, and I began, "Sir, the ways—"
Smith didn't listen. "What the hell took you so long?" he
said and dashed back up the stairs.

Gardner commented to me that he thought Smith had
been rather rude—and just then the sub was launched.
Everything seemed in motion. The great bow passed over us,
not quite cleaving down on us. Every horn and whistle in the
Yard went off. The sub fell away with awesome speed—and
suddenly there was nothing but this enormous space where
the sub had been. The water of the river backwashed up

into the building and quenched at the far end the hot smoking ways. The sponsor's party, looking ridiculous on its high isolated platform, departed.

Three weeks later, we did it all again on another sub, and three or four weeks later, again. This time, however, since it was the *Sea Robin,* to which I had been especially assigned, Smith put Watson in my coveralls and let me ride the sub down. So this time I stood on the deck of the sub near the bow, looking down at the sponsor's party, not quite able to see whoever it was wielding the bottle of champagne. Suddenly, the building began to move—but this was as impossible as that the great mass of the sub should move. A foreman yelled at me, "Holt onto sumpen'," and I turned to the stern, saluting the flag with one hand and holding onto a stanchion with the other. We *rushed* at the open wall, and blinked in the sunshine, and jerked to a sudden halt. It was that quick—over—the Hill behind us, the lovely placid eighteenth century of Portsmouth just there, across the water.

Some time after that, I wheedled my way to a one-day temporary order to sea duty, to a shakedown cruise of a sub. I don't know what there is about memory that this very exciting day should now be almost eclipsed from my mind. I remember the sunlight as we swung downriver and the bank of fog we slid into and the gulls that followed us. I remember about submerging, the toilet-rush of water in the hull tanks (my tanks), but no more sensation than that, no realization that we were in fact in a watery grave in the area where there still slept the men of the *Squalus,* which had submerged in 1939 forever. I remember that the submarine officers, a breed apart, were distant to anyone not in the submarine service; and once submerged, that we did nothing but sit at a table and drink coffee, the table rather small, the room noticeably without windows. Only that seemed strange.

Some years later on a two-week Naval Reserve cruise back

to Portsmouth, to the somnolent Yard, I was allowed in a
secret loft to see a full-scale wooden mockup of an atomic-
powered submarine. But all this was anticlimactic; for then
I was, as on the shakedown cruise, only a spectator. Still, I
had been involved, and the having been involved made all
of us conspirators. There was this intricacy, this complica-
tion of creating for the war a Moby Dick that would have
terrified Ahab, a great monster, jetting death—a beautiful,
foul obscenity, a magnificent evil, which was the essence of
the war.

EN ROUTE

~~~~~~~~~~~~~~~~~~~~

OVERNIGHT, FOR NO REASON, I was transferred to the South Boston Navy Yard. No housing was available, so I roomed with my sister north of Boston, in Malden. (She was sublimely happy with her first son and with the monthly return of her Navy husband from "milk-run" duty on the Atlantic, savoring the frequent reunions and separations.) I commuted. I took a B&M local to North Station, the MTA to South Station, a street car to the gates of the Yard, and a Yard bus to reach my duty station by 0800.

But there was no duty. I was supposed to learn about dry docks, but there was no one to teach me, and I couldn't have cared less about learning on my own. Invariably, I wound up at the end of the yard on a small, wooden, floating dry dock, just big enough to take a tug, but always empty. I was supposed to order the skeleton crew of two to "take her up and down a few times," but they swore that if we flooded the tanks, the "sum-a-bitchum" thing would never come up again. So the crew went on with its game of double solitaire, and I stayed out on deck alone, staring at the garbage in the bay, the gulls, and at the nauseous-smelling fish factory opposite. Daily, a woman in rubber smock and rubber gloves would step out of the fish factory onto a platform, strip off one rubber glove, and light a cigarette. Invariably, she would search for me, stare at me until she had finished her cigarette, then step back in the dark doorway for a moment and come out again, carrying a big fish. Then, silently, she would throw the fish at me. Always, the fish fell short, into the water. The gulls shrieked, the woman spat at me and went back inside. I felt doomed.

I had, in effect, chosen this. My commander at Portsmouth had ordered me in to discuss my periodic fitness report and to recommend me for promotion (more or less automatic) to the rank of lieutenant, junior grade. He had offered, if I were ever ordered away from Portsmouth, to pull strings and get my orders canceled. It was a splendid boost to my ego but when the orders did come, I did not put in a request to stay. The peak of submarine building had just passed in a flurry of cutback orders, and anyway my work had become routine. I think I left not because I wanted to get closer to the war, but because I wanted to see more of life, whatever it was. For in my first fifteen months in the Navy, on leaves and en route, I had managed to go the length of the East Coast—and there was life, somewhere there, in the war-motivated, restless busy-ness of simply going back and forth.

Cambridge. "Sure, I remember you. How the hell are you? What are you doing in this part of the country? Well, come on over."

Bernard DeVoto had been to Iowa to lecture on Mark Twain. I had been his student escort, and he had treated me as an equal. He had a native interest in moving people from the West to the East, and I was curious.

His house had the scale and the shaded ease of an old Iowa house, though few houses out there spilled over so with books. The real difference was in the Sunday-afternoon guests, the friends who dropped by for the infamous martinis: a famous author, a Boston editor, a Harvard professor, a female psychiatrist, a conscientious objector (whom I snubbed). I was no more than an oddity to them, but quite content to listen and get drunk on Culture by association.

Benny held court; he stimulated; he provoked. I studied his self-confidence. (I had thought success involved being distinguished and handsome; but Benny, with his upturned nostrils, was ugly. Touring a farm in Iowa, Benny had been transfixed by a cow staring at him, and said, "She sees the resemblance.") Idly, he took me up to educate me in the ways of the world. By some quirk of conversation he discovered that though I was going to the war I had never ("For God's sake!") shot a gun. So he insisted I come the next week to a summer place on Cape Ann, where he dutifully trained me in target shooting with a .22 and in the intervals lectured me on Thomas Wolfe. (*This* was life!)

New York. I had a great-uncle and aunt who lived in an apartment on West 81st Street. Trola was German, big, stocky, and dowdy. She made lists, itineraries, and we began to do New York with a Sunday service at Riverside Church. There, a platoon of fifteen ushers, millionaires all, marched us five miles to the servicemen's seats under the very nose of Dr. Harry Emerson Fosdick. Uncle Bou was French, small and quiet. He had a bad cold, but it was not until we were seated that Trola realized Bou was chewing raw garlic as a cold cure. That is why, dear Dr. Fosdick, people kept getting up in the middle of that service and moving away from the three of us, leaving us splendidly alone (and not with God either).

Uncle Bou was retired; he had been, I am proud to say

(speaking from my Iowa background), an interior decorator of yachts. He took me to the New York Yacht Club and had issued to me a visitor's card. I had only a glimpse of a high-ceilinged room with glass cases of ship models, for I was afraid to go back alone. I still have the card, twenty years later.

My college roommate, Webster, came up from Washington. We went one afternoon to the Frick Collection and heard the Budapest String Quartet with Piatigorsky and that night (tearing up Trola's list) went to McSorley's saloon in the Bowery. It was exactly as John Sloan had painted it, murky and odorous, and it was as if no one had moved since he had posed them, until we entered. Clearly, we were not wanted, but the bartender was decently cordial and served us two glasses of ale. No one offered to speak to us, and we left after one drink, but no one has moved in McSorley's saloon since that time.

Philadelphia. Web and I had been to see Robeson, Ferrer, and Hagen in *Othello*. It was all scarlet and gold and sonorous and sublime, and we cheered afterward and clapped until our hands burned. Then, still high with the sense of theater, we took a street car to Independence Hall, and though the night was foggy, the streets wet, the lamps crystalline, and we had the square to ourselves, our newly educated tastes were for both an earlier and a later violence. Besides, having delayed for this, we had missed the last train to Washington and had to spend most of the night upright in the station, drained of all emotion, utterly tired.

Years later, I read the lines of Henry James, who imagined some clever man saying there: "*What* an admirable place for a Declaration of something! What could one here—what *couldn't* one really declare? I say, why not our Independence?—capital thing always to declare, and before anyone gets in with anything tactless."

Washington. It was midsummer, humid beyond belief. We college friends rendezvoused at the Washington Monument, Web and Kenneth, Helen and Betty, and I. We found a bench in the shade, for I couldn't, in my whites, sit on the grass. We read aloud, solemnly, the new Eliot work ("Fare forward, travellers! not escaping from the past / Into different lives, or into any future"). Sweat trickled down my arm onto my leather watch band, and black drops stained my immaculate whites. In the cool dusk we sauntered down past the Navy buildings, along the reflection pool to the Lincoln Memorial. Suddenly, I sobbed like a child at my predicament, at the American predicament. Middle-aged, I still do—unable any more even to look at Lincoln, lest I disgrace myself with tears.

Richmond. There was an officers club here, and my temporary friend had led me here in search of Southern ladies, as if literature were true. And here they were! Lovely girls in flimsy organdy, clean, pure, with marvelous accents and lazy giggles of delight. ("Why, Robert E. Lee, I do declare!") We sat in the garden, rather barren, actually, but softly lighted with strings of Christmas lights on a grape arbor. We danced, moving slowly, familiarly, easily, to a three-man Negro orchestra. The friend in a grand gesture ordered sparkling burgundy (my first). When the club closed, the girls, because they were not allowed to leave with escorts, whispered with us and arranged to meet down the street. We must have expected a great mansion with white pillars; instead, they took us to their upstairs apartment and served us Coca-Cola. They were only secretaries in a tobacco company. They firmly resisted our advances. We parted, no closer than we had been while dancing.

A Southern town. I imagine some cloying sweetness in the air, of a mimosa tree, or the sudden bath of humidity,

or the unreality of a sleepless night; some such omen warned
me the minute I arrived that I had made a mistake. It had
been pleasant enough to receive letters from T——, a complete stranger, letters designed to entertain a serviceman,
letters half anecdote and half pencil sketches—neat sketches
of a yard boy, a cook, dogwood blossoms, the line of distant
hills, and a doctor with an enormous black bag. And T——
did me the honor of meeting the train; but something, the
lingering touch of his hand, a pitched intensity in his voice,
made me blurt out immediately that I couldn't stay, had
promised to go—that evening—well, then, at the latest, the
same train the next day.

Perhaps I only imagined that T—— was a homosexual.
My only experience had been ten years earlier when, one
summer night, a fat man had sat down by me on a bench in
the city park and suddenly cupped his hand over my pri-
vates, pressing down so hard I could not get away. Nothing
in T——'s letters had prepared me for his garrulous fa-
miliarity, his solicitousness, his elaborate celebration of my
arrival, but the connection with the earlier incident was
so automatic my mind closed right away. I would not, for
all my compassion, let T—— touch me again.

His house, set deeply in scrub pine, was much smaller
than I had imagined. I had thought the yard boy implied
affluence, but I could not see that the yard boy did more
than rake dead leaves into piles. The house was thick with
furniture, and there was but one bedroom, one unmade
bed. There would be nothing to do the entire day, T——
was that much of an invalid, but stay in the comparative
cool of the house and talk. So we talked, of the war and God
and Truth and whatnot, over a second breakfast with milk
in the coffee, over a late lunch with lemonade not quite
cold, into the sultry afternoon, on through a supper
thumped down by a surly black cook who came just for an
hour and then left us alone in the insect-filled night. By
then I was exhausted and silent. T—— offered grandly to

give me his bed; he might be able, he thought, to sleep on
the divan; in fact he insisted. I fought sleep for a long time,
but finally I slept as if drugged. I have the vaguest recol-
lection that sometime during the night T—— slipped into
bed with me and did I know not what.

Perhaps nothing. I am amused now by my concern, my
continued touchiness on the subject, my abhorrence, if you
will. If homosexuality was rife during the war and after,
I can understand its cause in some such loneliness as mine
and T——'s; nevertheless, I saw no evidence of it in the
rest of my wartime experiences, none whatever, though
there was talk about a certain pharmacist's mate and a
yeoman.

T—— acknowledged sadly at the train station the next
morning that though we had had a good talk, we had not
quite hit it off, had we? He clasped my right hand in both
of his hands and held on, until I made some excuse and
turned away.

Daytona Beach. It was midwinter. My great-aunt
and uncle had a house on the beach and an old but functioning Cadillac convertible. We had been to see a local
production of *Der Rosenkavalier* and had gone to an officers club afterward to drink daquiris and to meet a friend
of theirs, Naval Air Force Lieutenant M——. Dutifully,
politely, M—— invited me to tour the air base with him the
next day, and Trola whispered that he might be able to take
me *up.*

Dutifully, politely, I went with Lieutenant M—— to the
base, admired the rows of planes, the hangars, the runways,
the surrounding palm trees, but all the time yearned to go
up. Finally, casually, but grinning with his own pleasure,
M—— asked if I'd care to go *up,* and grinning just as
broadly, I said casually, why, yes, I guessed I would. The
matter of signing a form for the disposal of my remains did

not faze me, nor even the awkwardness of putting on a
parachute and trying to walk with the damn thing flopping
at my rear. I climbed into the two-seater SBD (Scout
Bomber Douglas) as if I did this daily, put on a helmet and
earphones, and *up* we went, over a jigsaw puzzle of lakes
and trees, and down presently to a tiny air strip in the midst
of a swamp. The air strip was marked out to the shape of
an aircraft-carrier landing deck, and M—— brought out
red-and-yellow paddles and cautioned me back beyond the
parked plane at the far end of the strip. Soon, three other
SBD's appeared in the sky, and one by one they practiced
their approaches to the "carrier." Lieutenant M—— posi-
tioned the hovering planes with his paddles; then each
roared down as if to land, M—— signaling to them their
apparent success before they roared off for another try.
When they had finished, M—— said, grinning again, that
we'd go back to the base a different route, if I'd like. Sure,
I said, anything.

Up we went and east to the coast and then north and
down with increasing speed along the white line of breakers.
And *down* some more until each separate wave was distinct,
and then *down* even more until we were just some twenty
feet off the ground and I could look *up* at the beach houses
on the dunes, whizzing by. Faster and faster, to some three
hundred miles an hour, till I roared with delight. *Hey, hey,
Iowa boy, look at me!* And then we headed *up* and *up* into
the blue sky and turned back west toward the air base.

As it turned out, we had to race a tropical storm to see
which of us would reach the base first. We landed in sunlight, but as if coming up against a solid wall of black cloud.
We ran for a hangar, steadying the parachutes with our
hands, but we were caught up in the violent gusts of wind
and sheets of rain and were soaked through instantly.

"You dumb jerk," Lieutenant M—— said, grinning, and
with great kindness, "You didn't know enough to be scared.
Hell, I was scared. I was so scared, I'm still scared." He

wiped the rain from his face and laughed, and I laughed—
and twenty-five years later *I* am scared.

The woman came out again to light up her cigarette, glancing at me first to be sure I was there and then
turning away scornfully. Her red rubber gloves and apron
glistened in the sunlight. And while I waited for her part-
ing indignity, I had to look at myself with some honesty.

All these travels up and down the East Coast had been
a reaction to middle-class poverty. I had not traveled much
before the war simply because there was not money for it;
a twenty-cent malt had been sufficient extravagance. But I
had always intended to travel—the honk-honk of the Diesel
train through my home town had been a daily reminder of
purpose—and my choice of architecture as a vocation,
which I could not practice in a small Iowa town, had been
calculated in that sense. It was not that I wanted to climb
out of my class, go from lower-middle to upper-middle or
anything like that; I only wanted to support myself and
thus be independent, as signified by travel or the ability to
travel. I looked on my Midwestern society as having been
essentially classless, with degrees of richness dependent
solely on effort.

It was a shock to me to see the fish woman, who would
not, could not, would never "travel," and must have known
it. No one such as I would ever rescue her from her daily
necessity; but while she acknowledged this hateful fact, she
still yearned for the impossible. I realize now that Iowa had
been *my* fish factory and that I had been rescued by the war.
To what purpose or advantage was not clear. There was
some smug satisfaction in my recent mobility, but there was
also the frustration of not having got anyplace. I seemed to
have moved from one fish factory to another, still im-
prisoned by the class boundaries of my own thought. Like
any serviceman brought to a certain pitch by this participa-

tion in adventure, I sought only thrill—physical, visual—
and this was a waste, for I had never learned really to feel or
to see. The superficiality of my travels is immediately evident and reducible to the cliché that I had not begun to
live. I hated and envied the fish woman her very expressive-
ness, as she hated and envied me my freedom.

Well, she threw her fish, and I turned away.

I wished myself back in Portsmouth, or anywhere, and in
a couple of weeks the magical orders came through, sending
me to a ship stationed in Bermuda.

BERMUDA

~~~~~~~~~~~~~~

THE SHIP I had been assigned to was a repair ship, a floating machine shop and storeroom, a miniature naval base with everything from twenty-foot metal lathes to a hospital operating room. Not so miniature, it was some six hundred feet long with a crew of nearly a thousand: three barbers, two shoe repairmen, some fifty cooks, twelve carpenters, eight laundrymen, six yeomen, and so on. I was one of twenty junior officers, ensigns or lieutenants junior grade, deck officers or specialists, and all Naval Reserve. (The senior officers were almost all Regular Navy.) We had double jobs, the operation of the ship and our own special assignments. Thus, I stood regular deck watches as Junior Officer of the Deck, and in the off hours had the care of a division of one hundred and thirty seamen—their records, promotions, work assignments, leaves, and so on. In addition, I was the "Assistant Repair Officer (Hull)," which identified loosely the work of my division: carpenters, ship-fitters, welders, sheet-metal workers, plus a small horde of second-class seamen who were learning these trades. And there were under me a jack-of-all-trades warrant officer and four chief petty officers, *between* me and the seamen. The warrant officer considered me unskilled and superfluous (I was, rather) and constantly bypassed me to deal directly with the Repair Officer, to my daily annoyance. I solved the problem months later by learning to bypass *him* and work directly with half a dozen first-class specialists—one old enough to have been a bootlegger in his youth, another a coal miner from Pennsylvania, another a goldsmith by former profession; these, I respected.

My quarters for nine months were, by any military standard, luxurious. I shared an eight- by-twelve-foot room with only one man. There were double bunks, a wash basin, two closets, one desk, two chairs, and a porthole (but the view out was completely obscured by a ventilating fan). My roommate was a radar specialist, a man from Brooklyn, affable enough but not really friendly. His Reserve commission was dated two or three days before mine, and so he pre-empted the lower bunk, where, uncommunicative by nature, he spent his leisure time reading murder mysteries.

I spent my spare time with two other j.g.'s down the corridor, but I did not in fact have any close friend. Rank prevented all but the most casual communication with anyone who had more than two stripes or less than one. The crew distrusted the officers, as well they might, separated by pay, education, living quarters, dining facilities, uniforms, work, and class background. Above me, the Repair Officer sneered openly at Reserve officers as, by definition, incompetents. Above him, the Executive Officer was simply overworked and harried. The Captain, like God, was unapproachable. And our chaplain had an ulcer.

It took me weeks, months, to make a place for myself on the ship or to feel that I was in any way "contributing to the war effort." And, of course, as long as we were in Bermuda, there was nothing much to do anyway.

No one in Bermuda believed very long in the existence of a war. (I wonder, twenty-some years later, if there is
any reality about a war beyond the scope of one's own experience.) No one in Bermuda even seemed much concerned. An enchantment lay over the islands. It was the spell
of Prospero, and this was the setting of *The Tempest*. The
sailboats, the sparkling coves, the houses in pink or blue
with white roofs, the horse carriages—the only war here was
between Caliban and Ferdinand, between lust and love,
over Miranda. But perhaps this moral war is related in some
way to that other war.

One day Mr. M——, a married man, under circumstances
I have forgotten, invited me to accompany him to a house
party. His friends were a mother his age and a daughter my
age. Mr. M—— had met them through the husband-father,
a retired American businessman. Mr. M—— said we were
invited to swim and to dine, and I did not hesitate to accept,
though it did surprise me when we got there to find that the
husband-father was "away on business." I think that we left
the ship after lunch and took a trolley of some sort along the
shore to the residence. (My memory is so hazy, probably
because of my mind's effort to forget the entire episode.) I
remember that the house was open and cool, that it was not
directly on the sea, but that we walked across a field and
down to a tiny cove of white sand, so surrounded by rocks
that the water hardly surged with the spent movement of
the ocean waves. Miranda, as I shall call her, was very blond
and tanned, shapely enough but rather plain, with small
talk of no consequence or interest. Nevertheless, the four
of us paired off and played in the ankle-deep sand or swam
in the crystalline water, Miranda and I touching hands
perhaps, nothing more. After swimming we drank rum
drinks and later ate some bland nameless fish and lolled in
the cool house past midnight—in fact, past the chance of
getting a ride back to the ship that night. No matter; we

could go in the morning after sleeping on the porch. Good nights were said, and we bedded down.

Presently, however, Mr. M—— got out of bed not very silently and headed across the living room and down the hall. I waited for him to return from the bathroom—and I waited. Slowly it dawned on me that he had gone to the room of the hostess and intended, had intended all along, to spend the rest of the night in her bed. Even more slowly still, it occurred to me that perhaps I had been selected by Mr. M—— solely for my usefulness in doing likewise with Miranda. And when I made that connection, although my mind revolted instantly, my body turned Caliban in stiff desire. If this were the plan, why the subterfuge of the beds on the porch? If it were not true, and I too went visiting, what outrage would follow?

Shakespeare's Prospero spent his idle time protecting his Miranda from a rape by Caliban, but guarded her only to turn her over to the first gentleman to appear, and him she promptly loved. When the entire shipwrecked company is at last made visible, Miranda exclaims, no doubt with a lusty squeal of delight:

> O, wonder!
> How many goodly creatures are there here!
> How beauteous mankind is! O brave new world,
> That has such people in't!

I like Prospero's sardonic comment following: " 'Tis new to thee," and think that Miranda stayed faithful not very long. Was my Miranda such a wanton lass? I'll never know. No double-meaning comments told me later if I were right or wrong. That Mr. M—— went back to visit, I know. That I was not invited back proves me right in supposition, wrong in action, more Ferdinand than Caliban, more foolish than smart. This much was clear: It was an age for Caliban.

"Now hear this: Loo-tenat jay-gee Lee, report to the quarter-deck." The musical phrase came out over the speaker system and was repeated, drowning out temporarily the sound of the movie. In anonymity was safety. Was an officer ever called away from his evening recreation unless he had done something wrong? I hurried below.

Lieutenant Commander K——, my immediate superior, waiting for me, rested his stomach against the guardrail and stared out at the rising moon. Even in that feeble light one could see the crisscross of wrinkles on his fat jowl and dominant jaw, the crafty look and texture of an alligator.

With a massive sigh he said to me, "Such a night. I should have got my hands on the captain's gig and two nurses *and* two bottles of champagne, well iced. I would have told that boat crew to head straight down the path of the moon, keeping a sharp lookout ahead, never mind what went on in the cabin. *Smell* the night," he ordered, inhaling deeply.

Frantz, my chief petty officer, and two of my shipfitters and Viglioni the welder hurried up to us, and with no directive whatever the lieutenant commander led us down the gangplank to a whaleboat waiting below. We cast off, and he raised his voice so he could be heard over the rising puttputt of the engine. "Those goddam movies have got you in a state of inertia. Ann Sheridan. By God, I've *met* Ann Sheridan. *Look* at that moon."

In fact the moonlight was now so bright that the movie screen had turned pale blue. Ahead, into the moon, we saw a seaplane take off into the night.

"Speaking of champagne, Lee, tell me—did you ever have champagne and strawberries? I once went to a garden fête over on Somerset. Lady Smith, someone like that, quite a big affair. Take a magnum of champagne, very dry champagne. Crush in a punch bowl a few berries, not many, add a smattering of powdered sugar—"

The boat slapped down on a wave, and spray wet us. Lieutenant Commander K—— roared blasphemy at the coxswain. We altered course, heading obliquely to the waves.

Presently, two black mountains loomed ahead—they were aircraft carriers. We steered past them and toward a dock, delineated by a tiny string of lights. Alongside the dock was a submarine—at least a black hulk low in the water. It looked like a submarine and then it didn't. There was something strange about the superstructure—and suddenly, like a clap of thunder in a clear night, I realized without being told that it was a captured enemy submarine.

When we had tied up, K—— motioned us close to him and asked in a whisper, "Which one is Viglione?" It was clear even by moonlight which one was Viglione. "Now, Viglione, you stay close to me. I may need some help with my Italian. We've got to be somewhat nice to these frickin' traitors. Lee, Frantz, I want you to measure that snorkel there, that breathing device. We want to build a fake one for one of our subs so the planes can practice spotting it. Come along."

It was a German sub with an Italian crew. It was the first one the U.S. had captured intact. On it was a large periscope-like device, a snorkel, which enabled the sub to run its Diesel engines while submerged.

Thus, briefly, there came to us in Bermuda a sense of the reality and excitement of a war.

NEW YORK

~~~~~~~~~~~~~~~~~~~~~~~~~~~~~~

THE FOG in the night was *present*—like the captain—inescapable, all-pervading, omniscient, and terrifying, an aura harmless in itself but capable of unnamable evils. The fog had forced us to anchor outside the Verrazano Narrows and wait for daylight. Radar would be installed on the ship when we got to the Brooklyn Navy Yard, but for now we waited and hoped nothing untoward would happen. It was my particular concern because, as Junior Officer of the Deck on the four-to-eight watch in the wheelhouse, the ship had been entrusted to my hands. Looking out the lowered window I could see nothing but the black night turning gray, displaying nothing but beads of moisture on every metallic surface. This alone was not horrific, but the din was. God knew how many ships were anchored close to us, waiting for the fog to lift with the daylight, or how many bell buoys and whistle buoys there were; but the buoys tolled and shrieked their warnings, and the ships responded in intermittent bell clangings, and something not very far off, deep-throated, sobbed. Atop our own wheelhouse, a solitary seaman clanged out set, vibrant, cacophonous strokes—so that in the wheelhouse we did not talk, but listened, and by listening tried to see in the night the unseeable terrors. And though the outer blackness soon turned to gray, the gray did not change to anything.

Who could sleep on such a night? One of the seamen luckily spotted the Captain before he surprised us and sang out, " 'Ten-shun!" and we froze into official positions.

Sleepless and dangerous, the Captain stalked to the window and stared out at the fog and listened to the sounds and then vented wrath.

"Lee!" (Leee-*ee*)

"Sir?"

"Who the hell told you to ring our bell like that?"

"The Exec. Sir." (Relief. Not *my* fault, whatever was wrong.)

"Get Bowditch." (*Who,* sir? I nearly said, my mind running through the ship's roster for some unfortunate seaman, the name vaguely familiar—but, of course, the *book!*) "That's not the way to sound the bell." (I've forgotten the proper way to ring the bell and will invent something.)

With book, by flashlight, he spelled out and confirmed our ONE-*one-two-three,* repeat-every-minute, but he objected to the length of the pause after the ONE, and ordered me up to instruct the seaman to do it *right*.

Hapless, I went out on deck. The racket of whistles, horns, and bells grew louder still. I found the ladder to the top deck, but at first there was nothing up there but gray ectoplasm, and for a time I couldn't even find the seaman. When I did, and instructed him, and he had changed the rhythm of our own soulful clang, I started back down, but stopped, realizing I was fated to be wrong.

Soon, like fate, the Captain came crawling up the ladder, the navigation book in his hand. I knew he would say, "By God, Lee, do I have to do it myself to get it right?" And he did say it, and he instructed me, and I reinstructed the seaman until the Captain was satisfied and went below for his coffee.

The seaman protested, "The Exec will be up here next, chew me out, and tell me to do it *his* way."

"Just do like the Captain says."

Wiping his hands on his buttocks, he said, "It's scary up here."

So I said the fog would lift soon and if he wanted liberty when we got to New York he'd better keep on doing just like the Captain said (*if* we got to New York, *if* the fog lifted, *if* when the fog lifted New York was still there).

The ship was to stand at its fogbound anchorage most of the morning. But a third of the men and officers were given ten-day shore leaves effective immediately. I was in that lucky third, and if my memory serves me right it took me just five minutes to pack, have my papers typed by a yeoman, and report on deck for departure. We were dropped into whaleboats, and the boats pushed off into the fog, rather like sticks cast adrift in a stream. Presently, however, the fog began to thin, and I saw under the most favorable circumstances the most beautiful sight in the world. There was Manhattan floating on the water and the cloud.

I keep that picture as if in one end of the inside of a shoe box that lights up at the press of a button. The box is lined with spun sugar, and when I put my eye to the peephole at the other end of the box and press the button, there is Manhattan again, as removed from the limitations of time and space as is the concept of God. The picture is compounded also by absence and yearning, homesickness, sleeplessness, the excitement of the sudden release, the noise of the bell buoys and gulls, the salt smell, the purple water —and I go back there again and again in memory and see

Manhattan as I saw it then, and always it is as if for the very first time.

I went home on leave, but I was impatient to get back to New York. It was the being away from home that was important, not the going back, and I discovered I would not want after the war to go back at all. Life *must* be in New York.

Our ship was in the Brooklyn Navy Yard for overhaul. At the end of each working day, we were free to leave the ship. Vogel, Bray, and I took the Yard bus to the gate, then the street car down Flushing Street and across Brooklyn Bridge (life! promise!), the subway to Grand Central, and then the shuttle across to Times Square. There were crowds of people. Virgil and Dante saw nothing more spectacular in Hell than those hundred thousand servicemen circling Times Square endlessly walking, continually replaced. Desperate, lonely, forlorn, but certain to find there the excitement for which they had gone to war.

Vogel, Bray, and I paraded about like board fences, rigid in our heavy bridge coats, never unbending, never very alive. In that guise it was possible never to meet a prostitute or a thief, and when drunk to be sober. The officers-and-gentlemen went to the theaters and the museums and the symphonies in chaste decorum—and yearned for life. We did this for four lonely weeks, and in that time picked up only one girl. In fact, she picked us up on the subway, a girl from Brooklyn, young, brash, not very pretty. When we tried to kiss her she skipped off. When she came to a subway stile, she ducked under it without paying. Vogel, Bray, and I were horror-struck. Nevertheless, like Kilroy, we were there. We could not have endured not having been there.

Our days were exciting, too. The ship was in a turmoil of overhaul. The decks were littered with welding cables. A steady stream of workers came up the gangplank to tackle some new stripping operation or rebuilding. The heating system went off, and the ship turned frigid. The water supply went off, and a steady stream of workers and sailors went down the gangplank to putrid makeshift toilets and returned again. Grime settled everywhere. Snow fell. Thirty minutes before the day shift ended, the workers quit and maneuvered to choice positions for a fast getaway the second the whistle blew.

Then I was given a job and went with three of my ship-fitters every day to Building 23. We were to sort through great files of blueprints of destroyers and destroyer escorts and select whatever sheets of structural detail might be useful in repair work later on. None of us knew what we were doing, but the work was warm and clean, and we were at one end of a room that held at least a hundred women.

Thus we were invited to their Christmas party. At two o'clock, the women stopped work and began to decorate their desks with tinsel and crepe paper. Out of desk drawers they hauled plates of cookies and candies and gifts to exchange. Radios were produced. Christmas lights were draped over typewriters. Meanwhile, the foreman, the only other male on the floor, took us into a vault, brought out a bottle, and poured raw whiskey down our throats. We emerged with all eyes on us and began a slow dance from one desk to the next, slow, that is, until one woman pointed out the mistletoe she had hung over her desk and demanded a kiss. Suddenly, we were in an orgy. I kissed, my God, I kissed a hundred women, two hundred women in an hour. I kissed a grandmother. I kissed a gorgeous Negress. I got kissed French-style, my first. I fondled breasts. Somebody screamed, and we chased the prettiest girls up and down the giant room, and then they chased us. They wiped their red lips across our cheeks and down across my white collar. They fondled us and kissed hard with their teeth. And then, at 3:30, stopped, decorously, and tidied up their desks. We staggered away, our lips a raw mass of cold sores for days to come—badges, envied by all the others on the ship.

Christmas Eve I want to forget. Vogel, Bray, and I did our duty at the Captain's cocktail party in the St. George Hotel, then made our way back to the ship, stopping at one deserted bar after another. We had to be back on board ship by midnight, for we were scheduled to be the junior officers of the deck on Christmas day. Did snow fall? And where would we be in another year's time?

Anxiety began to build in us, the fear that we would have to pay for our pleasures with our lives. The last third of the crew was due back from leave on December 29. Half a dozen men did not make it, choosing (their last free choice) to be AWOL rather than face whatever lay ahead. Every man in my division returned, even the man to whom I had illegally given twenty days' leave so he could "settle things" with his wife. But Lieutenant Commander K———did not return on the 29th.

On December 30, we moved (goodbye, Brooklyn Bridge, goodbye, Manhattan) to some godforsaken pier in New Jersey to take on fuel oil, some wilderness of dunes and oil refineries and the winter fog, now chill and ominous. There was nothing to do, nothing to look at, nothing except worry. The smoking lamp was out for twenty-four hours, and the ship reeked of the smell of oil.

Now that no one could leave the ship, the Captain announced what we had guessed anyway, that we were headed for the Panama Canal and then out into the Pacific, just where he wouldn't say. No matter. It was to certain death.

Late in the afternoon of December 31, the ship moved away from the dock and, under the direction of the pilot, out to sea, slowly, cautiously through the fog. When we were clear of land, the waves sudden and sure, we lay by to drop the pilot—and there on the boat for the pilot was Lieutenant Commander K———. The sea was so rough the pilot chose not to leave via a rope ladder, but to descend in a cargo net. We all crowded the rail to watch his departure and then the return of K———. Up he came, like a baboon in a cage, his arms loaded with champagne bottles and a huge paper bag of oranges. In the process of unloading him, someone stole his oranges, and as we headed off into the dusk, K—— roared threats over the speaker system, concerning the son of a bitch whoever he was who stole his oranges.

(Farewell America! I loved you!)

AT SEA

~~~~~~~~~~~~~~~~

AFTER TWENTY-FOUR HOURS of chaos
—everything tied down came loose, everyone was seasick
simultaneously—the ship settled down to a routine. Our
day began at sunrise with a call to general quarters, every
man at his battle station for a drill lasting some thirty
minutes or until the Captain was satisfied. Breakfast came
next—steak and eggs—and if the Captain felt like it, general
quarters was repeated in the midst of breakfast. Then work.
My one hundred and thirty men had to be assigned something to do throughout the day, and for a time that meant
cleaning and painting over the mess of reconstruction made
during the overhaul; later, the shipfitters went to work making ash trays and belt buckles out of stainless steel, and the
carpenters turned out lamp bases or whatever on their
lathes; the rest wrote letters (and I, like every other officer,
had to read and censor at least twenty letters a day). To add
to this, the Captain and the Repair Officer wanted further
work done. A watch-repair shop had to be designed (my
job) out of storage-locker space. An outside corridor athwart-

ships had to be roofed over with plate steel; the design was a beautiful problem because the slight flexing of the two dividing superstructure walls popped open any welding seam attempted. In addition, the Executive Officer had set up (not, I'm sure, on his own initiative) a training program for junior officers, such that at odd hours of the day we were ordered up for lessons in navigating, plotting courses, shooting the sun, and so on. But on top of all this was superimposed a watch schedule of four hours on and twelve hours off. So the day might begin with a sleepless midnight watch from twelve to four in the crowded, close radar room and end with a tense four-to-eight wheelhouse watch under the hypercritical eye of the Captain—with a general-quarters drill at dusk and perhaps another before the Captain retired. Quite soon I was able to fall asleep instantly, anywhere, any hour of the day or night, or go through the motions of general quarters without coming fully awake. I longed for just four hours of uninterrupted sleep in a bed that did not move. I staggered from one task to the next without thought for the morrow.

I suppose all this is analogous to life, our keeping so meaninglessly busy without any thought to the medium in which we moved or the direction. One reaches always for the stage of insensibility in sleep or for the consuming, masking routine such that death will be surcease. But I never examined what I was doing; I never wanted to. I would wade uneasily down the passageway and step out on deck only to be confronted by a massive green wall of water that sank slowly, replaced by a sunlit-silver sky. Clearly, neither of these insubstantial elements could support a steel ship, but I could think no further than that. Again, on the four-to-eight watch, when I had to make the rounds of the silent ship before dawn, moving from the tiers of sleepers out into the pitch night and lurching forward to the sleepy lookout in the bow of the ship, I was in such a mesmerized state it was as if I could keep on walking out onto those same planes, and there would be no change; for the ship was as insubstantial as the sea and the sky. We were protected only by our own dreams, comforted only by a sense of the beauty in which we moved.

We reached Panama, the tropics, maturity, and the Fall of Man simultaneously. The day we reached Balboa was oppressively hot, and the crew stripped off their T-shirts to reveal a nakedness as white as their shirts. Then they stood around, parboiling, watching the ship's slow process through the locks. Great black Negroes came out to toss heavy hawsers as easily as lassos, unconcerned by our fascination. The landscape fell away, the gates opened, and the hawsers were snaked back by the giant black men, who did not bother to watch us leave. We moved almost silently onto the high inland sea of the canal. Soon the shores encroached on either side, a myriad-shaded green, a jungle, dense and heavy. From the bridge deck we searched with binoculars for a color other than green, a burst of yellow blossoms or a streak of violet. Then Bray sang out, "I got a sloth!" and we all fixed on the direction he pointed, but saw only more green. Later in the day a radioman claimed an alligator, but we doubted him. After that, the jungle opened up to fields with the Army in it, and the Army watched us pass—guns, search-lights, radar antennae, jeeps, Quonset huts, tents—all silent except for the one man who idled out to yell, "Anybody from Boston?" and gossip with three or four of our men until he drifted away. It was dusk before we reached Panama City and dark before we tied up at a dock. We had wanted to see more, but for a time it looked as if we were going to have to move right out in the morning, and we spent a sweltering night in anticipation and disappointment.

But the next day, word was passed for all hands on deck that we would stay two days, liberty for half the crew each day, but Hear This! And the division officers were given to read a most extraordinary document issued by the local Navy commandant:

"Danger of Robbery—Precautions against. Conduct of Naval Personnel Visiting Republic of Panama. Riots and civil disturbances—Clearing Vicinity of. The Commandant is concerned about the number of incidents reported in which: (a) Naval personnel go on liberty with large sums of money on their persons, eventually to be the victims of thieves. (b) Naval personnel accompany unknown persons into alleys and other unfrequented places with the result that often they are beaten and robbed. It is suggested that Commanding Officers take such steps as are practicable to warn the personnel under their commands of the almost inevitable outcome of the above procedure, particularly if such personnel are even slightly intoxicated."

And so on. Following this, one of my saltiest CPO's volunteered to lecture my division on prophylaxis. He did this in such a manner that he raised expectations and erections.

One would think that the fact would have been less than the anticipation. Not so. The honky-tonk main street of Panama City was lined with bars, so close together the juke box of one was contrapuntal with the raucous sound of the next, and shops, shops with cameras, silk hose, liquor, handbags decorated with the stuffed heads of baby alligators, bracelets of Mexican silver, and jade supposedly from the Orient. And on the street, men carried open cases of watches from Switzerland or necklaces displayed along the length of their outstretched arms.

There on the street a photographer disappeared under his black hood to focus his camera on five seamen from our ship. They stood close together, arms linked over one another's shoulders. Smith, on the end, a burly man, was pestered by a drunken Indian woman in a faded purple cotton dress. She tried to kiss him. He pushed her off and

stared rigidly at the camera. She bent down behind him and
sank her teeth into his buttock.

In midafternoon the pack of officers I was with, having
finished shopping, began to drink. I remember one corner
bar, cool and pleasant with little round tables and assorted
rickety chairs. We listened with more amusement than
interest to the solicitations of young boys concerning their
"seesters." Lieutenant N——, an enormous man, leaned
with his back against the bar, supported by his elbows, his
drink in one hand, a cigarette in the other. A large woman,
a woman almost as big as the lieutenant, moved from table
to table, idly swinging her handbag, making her way to
the bar. She appraised the lieutenant and then suddenly
swung her arm. The handbag smacked him, as we say, in
the balls. "Come on, beeg boy," she cried, "let's go." And go
he did.

Our diminished pack ate dinner somewhere and then
found a bar that advertised entertainment. We were indeed
entertained by a skinny woman in black panties and bra;
her dance involved a red scarf that she put between her legs
and rode suggestively. We wanted more than that, but the
next act involved only a couple who danced with filled wine
glasses balanced on their heads, so we left. On the urging of a
boy in the street, we moved to a night club where one could
dance with hostesses before and after the entertainment.
The girls did indeed sit at our table and drink with us and
dance with us, and though I danced with a lithesome plati-
num blonde in a satin dress, I fail to remember what color
the dress was or what we talked about, fail to remember anything about the show that followed until the final number
called "Cocaine," in which the same girl came back to our
table and shook her giant naked breasts in my face.

Later still that night, we emerged onto the street and
found it lined with vintage taxis, their drivers urging us
to drive to the House of Love or wherever, and then we discovered en route to the ship that we had not been on the

main street, that the *night* main street was a row, seemingly a mile long, of adjoining apartments, and that the front wall of each building was made of shutters, which were drawn in slits of light or flung open the width of the room to reveal in state the same prostitute repeated over and over again. The scene is as hazy now as it was then, but the next night stands in my memory with terrible clarity. Dressed stiffly in whites as JOOD, I waited at the gangplank for the second liberty party to return, waited, listening to the suck of water between the ship and the dock and smelling from a nearby warehouse the unaccountable country odor of baled hay. Then they came, white figures against the black warehouses, singing, laughing, weaving their way up to the glaring deck light, which revealed their red faces and their unfocused eyes. The white uniforms were dirty. This man had lost his hat, another his shoes. They carried pictures made of butter-fly wings, or coconuts, or the alligator handbags, or red bananas, or bottles of rum, which we had to confiscate. They turned into the deck watch certificates of prophylaxis—venereal disease was an offense to the Navy if there was no prior evidence of preventive treatment—each of them, all of them, almost without exception, age thirty or age eighteen, joined thus in manhood, forever to be haunted by this memory of a life beside which the postwar life would always be pale. A Shore Patrol jeep drove up below us and dumped out two upright men and one horizontal. The two carried the third up the gangplank and lowered him to the deck while they cursed the Panama police, who had, supposedly, used night sticks on them and then robbed them. They had apparently been sprinkled all over with their own blood, one man's lip split open, his eyes nearly swollen shut. The man on the deck raised himself, heaved, and vomited in his own lap. After a time we got the mess cleaned up, and I turned away to try to smell again the nostalgic hay odor of the night.

When we left Panama, the word came over the PA system that we were headed for Pearl Harbor; when we left there, that we were bound for Eniwetok; but when Eniwetok lay to starboard, the orders were changed abruptly: we were to head for Saipan. It is hard, these twenty-some years later, with the knowledge that I did in fact survive the war, to realize the awful fear that the mere place names struck in me—in us. But at that time there had been no landings beyond Saipan, and no doubt there would be soon another island invasion and another and another; and so we moved in spite of ourselves to the very heart of the Japanese war, increasing every day the depth of certainty that we, that *I,* would not come back. Therefore, I am hard put to explain why those weeks at sea have turned out to be the happiest weeks of my life.

Some change must have taken place at Panama or shortly after we left. The sea had changed, for one thing. It had grown larger, more stately, more colorful. We moved for a week at a time without seeing land or a plane or another ship. Our bulky ship did not move very fast under any condition, but after a few days without landmarks, with nothing but the short increments marked on the navigation chart, there was the increasing feeling that we did not in fact move at all—a marvelous timeless feeling, aided by the half-awake, half-asleep state induced by four hours on watch and twelve hours off, around the clock. Furthermore, we began a zigzag course designed to bewilder any possible trailing submarine (designed to strike terror in the crew, even without any sign of a submarine). Using secret books brought to the deck house officiously by the security officer, the JOOD sounded out at varying time intervals the varying course changes that had to be executed promptly and precisely, lest the navigation officer lose all notion of where we were. Thus, we seemed to chop away at the center of the sea, now here, now there, but never with any sense of forward movement, except for that lurking fear that with one mistaken zag we might sail off the edge of the world.

Then, of course, the sea changed constantly. The Atlantic had been either green or gray, but never blue. The Pacific rang every conceivable change of blue in every texture into which water could be shaped. One day we ran onto such mountainous blue swells that the ship could not be held to its course. Waves are one thing, of a certain size, from a certain direction; swells are something else: an upheaval of the firmament, erratic earthquakes of an unimaginable proportion—the water shaped into mountains that sank suddenly into abysses—all this without the sound of wind or apparent cause, nothing but this gorgeous blue-black rolling world. And then the next day would be halcyon.

One day we hailed a sailing vessel, as strange as if we had spied Venus rising from the waves. Early in the morning, before light, we picked up the blip on the radar screen of something far off to port and moving at some three or four knots. Through binoculars, at dawn, we could see the delicate masts, the tiny myriad sails. God bless our Captain, he abandoned the war immediately and ordered us on an interception course so that we could inspect this relic of the past. Did he doubt it was real? Slowly, all morning long, we worked to close the distance between us until finally we were alongside. A four-masted schooner it was, all sails on, sailors in the rigging who waved, to establish our reality. The blinker light identified her as bound for New Zealand with a cargo of grain, and then she dropped off to stern and in the late afternoon disappeared forever.

My sons will never see such beauty unless they read Conrad or Melville, and if they do they may realize the depth of such beauty as well. The next day after the schooner we had "inspection at 1300," which means that the entire crew, all in whites, lined up on deck by divisions for roll call and for no other reason that I can think of. I see it all in such a glare of noontime light that the white uniforms have turned

pink and the shadows purple. I leaned with pleasure against
the rail while my one hundred and thirty men stood at attention and sounded off in their rigid blinding rows. Suddenly, the rows wavered and broke. I yelled, "'Ten-shun!"
but they ignored me. I panicked at this mutiny, until someone turned me around to look out and down to see what
they had seen—a whale. I shake off again my disbelief as the
entire crew crowded to the rail and stared down at the
monstrous hump of a gray whale surfaced in curiosity to
inspect us. It was quite simply phallic and obscene. I know
that *now,* having lectured on *Moby Dick* for years. The
counterpart of beauty is an inseparable obscenity—it is the
meaning of the schooner and the whale.

Most of those days at sea went on without incident, with
nothing to mark the sense of change. My pleasure depended
in part on a change of status. I had brought water colors and
good paper with me, and after the schooner I turned out
a small blue sketch of it, and after Pearl Harbor I was able
to paint a garish likeness of our own ship at anchor, with
the mountains of Hawaii in the background, green against
blue. These did not take long to do, and I could duplicate
them for ten or twenty dollars or, as it turned out, on the
order of my immediate superior and that of the Exec and
the Captain. My carpenters were kept busy making picture
frames. The point is that I was no longer threatened by my
superiors, for I could do what they could not do themselves.
I had arrived.

For example, on the 1200 to 1600 radar watch in the
windowless room behind the wheelhouse. The radar screen
showed no pips, but it did show the shapes of rain squalls
spotted here and there on the circle. The Captain's voice
came over the intercom: "Lee-*ee?* You see that squall just
off the starboard bow? Very well, now tell me if we're going
to run into it and at what time."

Quickly I ran two checks for the speed and course of the
squall, plotting them with wax pencil on a plastic board,

correcting for the forthcoming change of zig and zag. I
calculated and called back, "Captain? Prediction is for rain
on deck in about—seven minutes."

He yelled back, "Get the hell out here!"

Without much anxiety, I moved from the dark room into
the blinding sunlight of the wheelhouse and saw the white
sheets of rain suddenly hiding our bow.

"I should have said seven minutes more or less."

"Try again," the Captain answered, not unpleasantly, but
soberly. "We'd be in a hell of a mess if that squall was an
enemy plane."

The watch from 0400 to 0800 on our last night at sea
was something else. The Captain had stayed up all night,
his finger on the intercom switch to the radar room, and
poor Bray on the midnight watch did not have a moment's
peace. I entered the radar room, as if swimming through the
heavy smoky atmosphere, promptly at 0355; Bray, after ac-
cusing me of being late, filled me in.

The radar screen showed several blips, all friendly, but
"too goddam close for comfort. This is a fast bastard behind
us; keep the Captain informed. Don't try to plot any planes
any more. And here, look, this is a DE, we think. Watch for
land ahead. The old bastard will shit all over the deck if he
sees land before you do. Are you ready to relieve the watch?"

But Bray did not leave, he was too worried, and I took
over the nervous conversation on the intercom. There were,
I think, four seamen at work in the room, but we all took
our cues from the man seated in front of the ten-inch circular screen. Normally, the scanner, a radius line, swept
around the circle (our ship at the center of the circle) leaving a trail of light-green "snow" and bright spots, which
were ships or "bogies"—something unidentified. The scanner could be stopped and adjusted to sweep a small arc to
pinpoint the bogey. Another device gave more or less ac-

curate information on the distance away of the blip. Distance away and angle, the information was transferred to
a plotting board and, with repeated readings, translated into
the bogey's course and speed, the information then relayed
over the intercom to the impatient Captain.

That night there were half a dozen blips to watch simultaneously. All the ships were converging on the strait, a
mile wide, between Saipan and Tinian. When some kind
of patrol vessel came out to meet us, look us over, setting
what looked like a collision course with us, the Captain
got a little upset. By 0500, however, we had the strait at
the top of the radar screen. By 0600, the Captain curtailed
our information; he had enough light to see by without our
guidance. So there was nothing for us to do but watch the
progress on the radar—the coastlines approaching, growing
distinct, one island gradually falling to each side of the
screen as the strait drew closer and widened.

Then we were through, and the men in the room jammed
tight around the radar, staring, swearing—the only way to
express our amazement. The normally dark screen was alive.
The scanner on each swing lit up scores of blips, hundreds
of blips, so many they could not possibly be ships, and yet
they were ships, *hundreds* of ships assembling in the bay on
the west side of Saipan for the imminent invasion of Iwo
Jima.

When I was relieved at 0800, I could go out on deck and
verify with my own eyes what had seemed so unbelievable,
but what was now so real.

I had come to the war at last.

February 1945-
August 1945

SAIPAN

~~~~~~~~~~~~~~~~~~~

THE NEXT FEW DAYS were nightmarish;
the combination of physical exhaustion and lack of sleep
distorted everything. I did not in fact tour every ship in the
bay, an aggregation of craft far outnumbering the Spanish
Armada, the ships and landing craft that went off to the
invasion of Iwo Jima, but it seemed in retrospect that I had
commandeered a whaleboat and personally visited a thousand ships (by rope ladder each) to inquire of their needs,
to arrange some kind of repair work before they left—and
I have no sure way to sort out what I in fact did and what I
imagined I did.

Even before we anchored, the ship-to-ship radio was busy
setting up work for our repair ship. "Hello, Tomcat, hello
Tomcat, this is Ajax, this is Ajax, message for you, message
for you, over," and at the sight of us, other ships in the harbor sent messages over to us by boat. A power board was on
the blink; could we send an electrician to check it? Another,
the radar was off; did we have a technician on board? An
AKA had a broken shaft; could we turn one out on a lathe
before midnight? Then headquarters ordered an inspection
of ten LST's (Landing Ships, Transport) somewhere in the
harbor—send an officer at once. (Lee-*ee!*)

All that day and half the night and all the next day, I
toured the harbor. At each LST, I climbed the Jacob's ladder and found the First Lieutenant and asked if the ship
could go through with the operation under her present
condition, and always something was wrong. This one
needed a length of cable, which we had in our stores. Another needed a pelican hook repaired, which we could do.
On another, the bow doors weren't opening properly and
the ramp wouldn't come down. So let's take a look at it.

There were three hundred Marines jammed onto the
forward deck of the LST. Not only that, the deck held guns,
boats, supplies, rations, ammunition, barrels of gasoline,
medical supplies, tents, and radio equipment. A twelve-inch
board extended from the deck house to the bow, and that
space had to be kept clear. Everything else was jammed with
men, so close they could not all lie down at the same time,
and when a rain squall hit, they had no choice but to be
soaked through. They had been this way for three weeks and
shortly they would leave for Iwo Jima. I saw them! Some
were asleep in the sunlight, others looking at a *Life* magazine two months old or reading a torn pocket book or much-
read letters. Others were cleaning and recleaning their rifles,
or getting their hair cut. They wore green undershirts or
none at all. They had tattooed on their arms "Semper
Fidelis" or "USMC." They had discarded their camouflaged

helmets and their boots. Every one of them seemed to be just eighteen years old.

The First Lieutenant and I walked to the bow and down through a hatch and tried to find what was wrong. By accident, we found that a cotter pin was missing, and in ten minutes the work was done.

Another LST had to be brought alongside our ship for half a dozen major jobs, all in a hurry. The First Lieutenant wore his hat on the back of his head. He was unshaven, very tired.

"This goddam tub rolls, see, pitches. The waves are like this, see, and the fucking ship here headed into them. Then this wave comes at us sideways. Like it picked us out, and *slaps*, all at once, from there to here. Christ, we keeled over and we rode on our side for so long I damn near jumped. See, this bracket."

The boat davit was bent. It would have to be cut with an acetylene torch and rewelded. However, two feet away was a stack of four-inch shells.

"What's holding these shells?"

"*Christ* is holding those fucking shells. Wait'll I get the Loo-ten-ut Jones. They're his goddam shells."

A Marine lieutenant, shaven, impeccable, his campaign hat anchored neatly on his eyebrow. I was introduced.

"Pleasure to be here. How's about fixing this?"

"Well, we can do it, sure enough," I said, "but the sparks will be all over those shells. You'll have to move all that."

"We've got to heave off you at 1600. That's an hour," the Marine answered. "Lieutenant, you get you your welder. I'll take care of the shells."

It took some time to find a welder (Viglione) and get his cutting torch and tanks and welding cable across to the ship alongside. Meanwhile, the Marine lieutenant found a tarpaulin and secured it between the twisted bracket and the stack of shells. He wet down the tarpaulin with a bucket (Viglione trying to keep the bracket dry). Then he refilled the bucket and from the crowd of spectators motioned to a Marine private and then maneuvered him into position.

"You. You keep that tarp wet. Don't do anything else. Don't move from there till I tell you to move. Don't even look at anything but that tarp. Keep that tarp wet. Is that clear?"

"Yes, sir!" The boy took his stance—he looked like he was sixteen.

The cutting went smoothly, but the minute Viglione began to weld, the sparks flying onto the tarp, we heard over the speaker system. "Now hear this! Air raid alert! Now hear this! Air raid alert!" I looked about uneasily, but I was the only person who did. North of us, several ships manufactured smoke. The stiff wind soon carried the smoke down to us, smoke so thick we could not see the ship alongside. Shortly after that, general quarters sounded, the horns of both ships quacking. Pandemonium. The Navy crews ran to their battle stations (the crowded Marines could not move from the open deck).

Under his mask, Viglione could not hear the horns and kept on welding, and the Marine fire guard did not move. Jones looked at the sky and shrugged, then fished a cigarette out of his pocket. My battle station was below deck at a damage-control locker along with half a dozen others. I decided I'd better stay with Viglione. When he pushed back his mask to fit on a new welding rod, he looked around in bewilderment at the men with their helmets on, alert at the Bofors gun. I told him it was a drill, to keep welding. The young Marine slopped water onto the smoking tarp.

Five minutes later, the all-clear sounded, and the Marine lieutenant drifted away somewhere. Five minutes after that, Viglione finished and began to scrape the weld. I spoke to the Marine private, who did not turn when I spoke. "OK," I said, "no more sparks." And realized he would not move, no matter what I said, until Lieutenant Jones came back and released him.

When Jones did come back, he took Viglione's steel brush and inspected the weld himself and then without a word he handed the brush back. Then he said to me, "We still got time for a cup of coffee, Lieutenant." And then he looked for a long minute at the motionless boy with the bucket poised over the tarpaulin and finally he said something sharply, and the boy moved and put the bucket down and clicked his bare heels and saluted grandly—and waited for Jones, leisurely, to return the salute.

Then they disappeared, the ships, the Marines, and the harbor turned into a continuous Sunday afternoon. The armada had left for Iwo Jima, to make history. The rest of us caught up on our sleep and then rigged the movie screen. At night there was not even a blackout on ship or on shore. The only planes in the sky were our own B-29's.

The Captain, somebody, discovered that the only plane the junior officers could identify was the B-29 and so instituted (at once!) a course in aircraft identification to be held in the officers' mess *during* the movie. Some ingenious arrangement flashed photos of aircraft onto a screen for a tenth of a second, some such nonsense, and we were supposed to call out the identification before a second picture appeared. The film was repeated over and over, the interval of flash progressively reduced. We soon learned to identify the sequence and the scenic backgrounds rather than the fifty or so silhouetted planes and in that way satisfy the poor Exec who had been given the task of training us. The Exec discovered the ruse and ordered us all to stand aircraft watches during the day on top of the ship, with binoculars and a logbook at hand. But *every* plane in the sky was the easily identified B-29, and we soon discovered that the Exec did not climb up to check on us or even inspect our logs, and so we used the isolated deck for sunbathing or to catch up on our sleep—that is, after the first excitement had worn off. We had gone from hectic activity to a restless lull without time to absorb what we had seen.

I took my water colors up on my aircraft watch and essayed to record where we were. The prevailing wind held our anchored ship pointed north generally, but moved the scenery back and forth in a panorama, in two panoramas, one on each side. To port, the open ocean, fresh, purple, and white-capped, immense and featureless, except for the tops of two Japanese freighters sunk close by in the bay. The rusted elongated stacks were upright but sitting in the water, a junk yard visited by occasional souvenir hunters or some sea bird. To starboard was the bay and Saipan. The water of the bay, calmer than the open ocean, reflected the green of the hills beyond or showed turquoise at the shoreline. When we first got there, there seemed to be more ships than water. Now, in the interval of the invasion, every ship was gone but the auxilliary vessels like ours.

The wind calmed, the sun was suddenly hot, then the wind shifted, and everything circled around busily. After a few minutes the bay lay to port, and I tried again.

Buildings edged the bay. At the water's edge, trees were distinguishable, the trunks of palm trees (the fronds all shot off in the invasion of Saipan six months ago). It was then a beach head; now it had become the recreational area for several thousand enlisted men. (One of the periodic chores of a junior officer was to draw some seventeen cases of beer from the ship's refrigerator and to accompany beer and men to the beach and sell the beer; in this way I heard the rumor of the bather who located a shoe—with a foot in it.) Behind the recreation area was a town of sorts, then more buildings, Quonset huts mostly, stacked up in the red areas between the hills. The hills descended into low mountains, all lush green, deep green, with superb full curves and blue shadows.

To the south and east, way back behind the recreation area, was the long flat area of the airfield. For all the color and activity in the foreground, it was that flat hazy area to the southeast that dominated—and the sky above where two or three planes circled, waiting to land—gray against gray— the long line of body, the great upright fin, hanging suspended in the sky—dominated because the planes were back in midafternoon from their fire-bomb raids on Tokyo. They were the feature of the landscape, and the heart yearned after them in a terrible glee.

Some days later, I saw the B-29's at closer range. Another thing the junior officers had to do, periodically and inexplicably (Who's in charge here? To whom are we attached?), was to spend a day on Shore Patrol, traveling over the island in a jeep with a luckless Army lieutenant assigned to the same task. We did in fact nothing by way of patrol, but we saw the entire island, climbing up those terraced hills to visit one endless camp after the other, or down into the town where the houses were like movie sets with only one wall standing (and we stopped in the rubble, attracted by the blowing paper, which turned out to be paper Japanese money; we gathered it up and later sold it for souvenirs). Then we went on south through the camps of civilians (Japanese? Saipanians? Is there such a name?), past ragamuffin children who held out their hands to us or thumbed their noses, and right on until we were stopped by an obnoxious guard who threatened us with a machine gun and ordered us back. We parked and watched for a while the B-29's return. Incredibly, they were framed by a Japanese *torii*, tipsy and bullet-scarred, red paint flaking, but whose lovely shapes contained the runway—and the planes came in one after the other, with an engine smoking or, clearly, a section of the tail fin missing. I have seen them! It was terrible; it was grand.

One morning, after the four-to-eight watch, exhausted, I went back to bed, stripping to my shorts, climbing into my upper bunk (which had just been straightened by a surly, colored steward), and fell asleep immediately. The ventilation fan in the porthole did not keep the room cool, so I was bathed in sweat and, as always, only half asleep. So there was no need for the Captain's orderly to say more than once, "Sir, the Captain wants to see you in his cabin, on the double."

Panic. The word is far too mild to indicate the Captain as godhead and my immediate sense of guilt (like Joseph K. in *The Trial*), along with the bewilderment of not knowing the crime. To paint a water color for the Captain was one thing, but to be summoned to his cabin was serious. I nearly dashed up in my underwear to prostrate myself and confess; instead, I dressed quickly, polished my shoes on my roommate's bedspread, then walked slowly, hoping I would appear cool and calm before the bar. The pip-squeak orderly, who spent his day in the corridor outside the Captain's cabin, looked at me disapprovingly and showed me in.

The Captain sat at table, folded his hands together over his mouth, and said, "Now, Lee, harrumph, tonight I'm going to have four nurses come aboard and I want you and A——, harrumph, and B—— and C—— to entertain them. Take them over to the Officers Club for a few drinks and then bring them to my cabin for dinner, harrumph. Then we'll go to the movie, and you young fellows, cough-cough, can take them back to their quarters afterward."

"Yes, sir."

Saved from the gallows, I exited (backward, bowing), savoring the sight of a most nervous A—— waiting his turn to appear before the Captain. A——, B——, C——, and I got together in the mess to compare notes, but there were no variations in the story, harrumph-harrumph, and so we immediately broadcast to every other junior officer on board that the four youngest, handsomest officers had been honored by the Captain in person, etc., etc., and spent the rest of the day shaving, showering, and donning our dress whites. At 1530, the Captain's gig waited for us at the gangplank, a gazebo of a boat, with white curtains, tassels, the brasswork as polished as we were. At the dock, the Captain's station wagon and driver waited for us and took us up the winding road to a naval hospital (inevitably, Quonset huts) and to our blind dates.

They were in khakis, interchangeable as far as ordinary looks were concerned, but obviously female, and it had been a long time. There were only three of them, but A—— soon solved the problem by getting so drunk he couldn't join us for dinner. Meanwhile, we got our whites all wrinkled getting us all into the station wagon and down to the club, content simply to touch the opposite sex.

The club (inevitably, Quonset huts) was precisely forty-five feet by two hundred and forty feet, surely the longest bar in the world. Enlisted men, separated by a solid wall from the officers, could drink only beer at ten cents a can. Officers could get whiskey for twenty-five cents; whether you asked for bourbon or for Scotch, you got Three Feathers and no mix. But the bar was crowded, and all eyes were on us, and we did our duty. My date did not drink, but the rest of us steeled ourselves against the Captain's dinner.

Back on ship (poor A——, disgracing himself on the gangplank, under the stare of Old Hawkeye), flustered, we presented ourselves to the Captain and went up to his cabin. His table was stunning, down to the bougainvillaea in the center. The stewards, all sweaty and nervous, began to serve from silver trays. We had fruit cup, French onion soup, filet mignon, browned potatoes, broccoli, fresh (frozen) peas, rolls, ice cream, cake, coffee and cashew nuts in individual silver bonbon dishes. All this took us past the regular movie hour, but of course the entire crew waited until we filed out on deck and were quite ready.

During the movie (for the record, it was *Shine on Harvest Moon* with Ann Sheridan), the nurses took turns using the Captain's shower, a great luxury for them. Midway through the movie, a downpour. When the rain stopped, a small USO troupe appeared, all male: a three-man band, an imitator (who ended with a hula dance), a magician, and a juggler who could do little in the wind following the rain. We kept disappearing, I might add, down to A——'s cabin, where he had brought out whiskey from his desk safe and resumed drinking; there was great whispering with the nurses to entice them down there, but only one came, and she was intent solely on getting tanked. The Captain had the good grace not to say anything when we reappeared. And in due time the movie resumed, ending somewhere around midnight. The Captain then presented the senior nurse with half a dozen ash trays made from brass stock, beautifully turned on a metal lathe, and escorted the party to the gangplank. In the transfer to the gig, the senior nurse accidentally dropped the ash trays in the bay. Luckily, Old Hawkeye had hurried off to bed.

Then, at last, began the good-natured, intense fumbling at breasts—the water choppy, all of us tossed back and forth, half sick, half drunk; and on the ride back up the hillside, more of the same. The driver obligingly parked so that we had a view of the bay, the tiny lights, red and green, the sea glazed with moonlight. But in a minute or two the nurses stumbled out of the car and left us shaken, soiled, stiff and happy with unfulfilled desire. We headed back to the ship and to A——'s room, taking turns going "harrumph-harrumph" all the way.

The next day, from the ship we could see a line of toylike ambulances (the red cross on the white field) at the dock, waiting for Navy amphibians to land. And our work resumed.

There came limping back into port a cargo ship with a list to starboard of forty-five degrees. In the dark she had been rammed amidships by her own destroyer escort and immediately took on water. I went along on the inspection party and then took charge of the details of repair.

We floated a barge alongside the vessel and from it sent divers down to fit a tailor-made cofferdam over the hole. Once this was snugly in place, the water could be pumped out of the hold, righting the ship so that the cargo could be removed, would have to be removed before permanent repairs were attempted, for the flooded hold contained thousands of barrels of aviation gasoline, the buoyant barrels still loosely stacked but floating in the cavernous hold. The job was routine enough except for the gas; the hold stank of the gas, and my crew dared not light a torch, or a cigarette, or scrape metal on metal. And it was an around-the-clock job. I did little myself but hold my breath all day and all night. The merchant-ship mate kept an eye on his personnel, and we frequently went to his closed cabin where it was safe to heat coffee and to smoke cigarettes. Even there, we could hear the pumps throbbing and we were conscious, hour after hour, of the ship's slow return to an even keel. Toward dawn, after a breath of fresh air, we climbed down into the hold, a darkness hardly touched by a solitary safety light. Was the cofferdam holding? When could we begin unloading? But neither of us thought to ask what would happen when the water level inside the hold reached the point where the gasoline drums lost their buoyancy. There had to be that moment of settling down, and it came while the mate and I stood on top of the floating barrels. They settled down all at once. Great grinding noises, barrels falling over, crashing, a roar—we were both thrown off our feet into the slime—and I closed my eyes against the dark, which I feared would momentarily become pure flame. That quickly, though, it was over. We climbed out of the hold, the mate saying casually and with suitable expletives that we shouldn't, after that, be alive, now, should we?

I tried to get killed again a week later. We brought alongside our ship a destroyer escort that had taken a bomb amidships, killing twenty-eight men in the mess hall on the main deck and in the engine room directly below it. The ship's port engine room was able to function, however, and our job was simply to patch up the gaping hole and make the ship watertight so she could make her own way back to the nearest navy yard (at Pearl Harbor, two thousand miles away). My bosses came over to inspect the damage, trying to ignore the fact that the DE Captain and his officers were unshaven, dirty, wild-eyed, and drunk. The hole in the deck was a frightful thing, some fifteen feet across and fifty feet long. Deck plates were twisted upward, torn, pierced by shrapnel, already rusting. The 'tween-deck rows of wiring hung from nothing, charred black. The structural beams, scantlings, which held the ship together, had snapped; we didn't have enough heavy steel to replace them. We conferred, pooled our experience, and decided that they could get by, would have to get by, with what we had. All this mess had to be cleared away; we'd throw in a few L-beams and then cover the whole area with plate to keep the sea out and send the ship on its merry goddam way since that was what its Captain wanted. Our Captain made arrangements for the remaining crew members to be fed and housed (and cleaned) on our ship and then left me in charge of the whole job.

I rounded up a gang of shipfitters and welders, and we went down to the gaping hole. God, the ship smelled like a garbage dump. We hardly knew where to begin. Before the ship's electrician left, we had him cut all the power on the ship. Then Smith (I'll call him) and I each grabbed a handle of a large cutter and reached up to cut the burned overhead wires.

But the power was not off. Luckily we were thrown downward immediately, breaking the circuit through us. A few sparks smoldered on our shirts, that was all. I felt rather as if the blood had been drained from my body, but I was more angry than hurt. The cutter blade had a hole at the cutting edge a quarter of an inch in diameter.

I sent for the electrician and in a fury sent him back to *cut the goddam power this time.* I think now that he was still so dazed by all that had happened to him (or that had happened to the twenty-eight others, more or less the same thing as happening to him)—I think he *intended* to kill us in retaliation. At any rate, the bastard came back in due time, profuse in his apologies and his assurances that this time the power was off, and then he stood there and watched us reach up with the cutter and *do it again.*

I was so stunned I could not breathe for a time. Smith, however, heaved the cutter in the direction of the electrician and scrambled after him, getting in about three good jabs to his face before he broke away.

We sat around after that on the grimy deck, Smith and I, smoking our cigarettes, looking at the two holes in the cutterblade, not saying much of anything.

I have a photograph of the repair work nearly completed. The flimsy bulkhead is in place to the left; the welds show clearly. The next-to-the-last deck plate is in place ready to weld. Five welders stand there, grinning at the camera. I cannot remember all their names. There is a trash barrel behind them, a fire extinguisher, an open box of welding rods, and the rubber hoses snake across the patched deck. Over the side on a wooden platform is the welder, Viglione (I will never forget *him*); he wears a leather jacket and heavy gloves; his helmet is tilted back to show to eternity his shining white teeth.

And there were more jobs like that, makeshift, urgent jobs, so that we worked day or night, or both. If our repair ship didn't have the necessary parts, we tried to get them from a supply depot, or we made them in our own

shops, or we borrowed (a vague term) from an Army base.
Our men were overworked. They began fighting among
themselves. Several from my division came to me demanding to be transferred, now, at once—and then went back to
work again.

I risked death a third time when I took a gang over to a
barge to do some cutting inside a tank. But the tank reeked
so of the gasoline it had formerly held that my men refused
to light their torches. We went back to the ship, got three
testing devices, checked them out by holding them near a
gasoline can, got good readings on them, returned to the
barge and held them inside the tank, got no readings—but

still my men refused to light their torches. Finally they got back into the whaleboat and backed away as I lowered myself into the odorous tank. After a bit, I struck a match, and since I was still there, I raised the match carefully out of the hole so the men could actually see it with their own eyes. But I hadn't wanted to do that.

I don't know—it went on and on like that. Not very long, a month perhaps; but long enough, more than enough.

B—— and I got the bright idea of getting some more brass ash trays to take up to the nurses. So we did. We dressed in fresh khakis, wangled first the motor launch to take us to the dock on official business and then the ship's jeep, without a driver. Our idea was to find the middle nurse, not the old biddy or my date, but the prettiest of the three, and for her to get a friend—we rehearsed the whole business as we drove up to the hospital, looking back and down with joy at our ship in the harbor, gray against a stunning blue sea.

We found our girl almost immediately—looking haggard —and wished we hadn't. On a porch, in the sunlight, there were wounded men, dressed in bright red or blue bathrobes, all bandaged on head or foot or chest, all silent, watching us.

The nurse recognized us.

"Oh, hello," she said.

"We brought you some more ash trays. Remember?"

She took them, her arm dipping with their weight.

"Oh, thanks," she said, and clutched the unwieldy package to her chest.

There was an awkward pause. B—— and I must have nudged each other expectantly.

She looked at us and then looked around her and looked back and said, "We're all pretty busy. Why don't you just go away now?"

We went souvenir hunting instead. I wish to God we hadn't. That afternoon has become not so much a nightmare as a half dream, shown to me repeatedly, as if in slow motion, or like the running one does in sleep, so hard and yet without progression, like wading waist-deep in water. Color became intense: the green light under the tall trees became a green glare so that I put my hand up to shield my eyes, and yet would look at the dark-blue shadows and the occasional spots of yellow sun. Everything became green, blue, and yellow, but mostly green. Even the light was frightening. We walked for some five minutes off the road, pushing against some mottled ground vine that made walking difficult. Overhead (so bright!) the tops of the towering trees were stirred by the sea wind; down where we were, there was a thick silence. We tried to see the ground, see where we put our feet; our feet disappeared in the underbrush, making no sound. If we were to yell, no one would hear. Equally, we did not want, suddenly, to make a sound. Only a few nights before, while watching the movie on deck, we had seen the yellow flashes of night fighting, which meant more Japanese flushed out of the caves of Saipan.

We carried no side arms. I wanted to go back. "No," said B——, "I tell you we'll find something." He whispered, as I had. So we went on.

Then, like a visitation, a cloud of butterflies drifted past, black, all black; rather, shades of black. Then they were gone. We followed a ravine, and the ground became mushy. We came to a clearing and looked around. "Look!" said B——. Ahead of us, a path, leading to a fissure in rock, to a cave. We started—and stopped. A toad heaved itself off the path, a mammoth toad. Then another, another—more —dozens!—the place was infested with toads, enormous toads. We stepped carefully through them, attracted, like the toads, to the cave. The black butterflies were near the fissure, on every leaf, motionless, every shrub. The mouth of the cave seemed as black as they, and we hesitated to enter. Also, there was a rotting smell, loathsome as the toads. But we could see wooden boxes, broken open, and the color of brass—cartridges. Inside, more boxes—mortar shells. Round land mines stacked like pancakes. A cloth hat. A part of a shoe. A bone. Also, there were snails over every-thing—terrible snails, as big as tennis balls—thousands and thousands of snails on the boxes, on the clothing, on saki bottles, on the rocks, on the ceiling, on the ground—*they* were the smell, and they moved, stirred, clacked against each other, climbed on top of each other, made giant balls of snails that broke off and clattered down.

When that handful of Japanese soldiers lived in that cave, were the snails there? Was a flame thrower used by whatever American platoon came wandering down the path? (And were the butterflies there?) How were the Japanese flushed from the cave without an explosion? (I *know* someone was killed there; I should think without noise; I know too the smell of death, its portents, its color.) Did someone dare speak? The confrontation. Some little atrocity. Someone begins to run. An American, his cigarette in his mouth, leisurely raises his rifle, his machine gun—a stitch of bullets, the running suddenly slower, dreamlike. A touch of red in all that yellow and green and blue. Or it was the childlike little men, clutching grenades to their stomachs. Or sucking through their teeth, watching the platoon approach the land mines on the path. When did the snails appear?

"Hey, Loo-ten-ut Lee. Ya got a minute? Could you come down to the shop? I wanna show ya somethin' I made."

Fox (I shall call him). Carpenter, second class. From somewhere in Wisconsin. Striking for first class, but a gold-bricker. Never any trouble with him, but he never seemed to be working. A solitary. Older than I was. Married. Always a friendly greeting and always that hint of obsequiousness and cleverness. The name "Fox" is apt.

It was after 1600, and the shop was empty. We had twelve carpenters, and they kept a neat shop, pleasant with the smell of wood and turpentine. I presumed Fox had finished the frame for my water color. Instead, he went to his locker and brought out a circular object covered with a stitched canvas, something like a top hat. With a flourish, he drew off the canvas.

He had turned out on the lathe a mahogany base some fifteen inches in diameter, stained and varnished it to a mirrorlike finish. Spaced precisely around the outer edge, wedged into holes drilled in the base, were a dozen rifle shells, polished. At the center, a post made from three Bofors shells. On the post, waxed, polished, a human skull.

"Damn you," I said. "Oh, God damn you."

"Whatsa matter?" he answered, thunderstruck and outraged. "I thought you'd like it. Lookit the work I did on it."

"Oh, God damn you, Fox, you either throw that overboard or you keep it out of my sight, you understand? I'm going to check on you every day, day or night. I'm going to drop in here any time and if I catch you showing that God-damned thing to anybody, to anybody at all, I'm going to—I don't know what I'm going to do, and you can just keep guessing as to what in hell I might do. You understand that, Fox? Understand? Oh, damn you, God damn you, Fox!"

ULITHI

~~~~~~~~~~~~~~~

AHAB HAS JUST ROUSED his crew to the chase for Moby Dick. The crew that evening turns to chants and dancing. Ahab retires alone to his cabin in the fantail and watches the sunset. He laments because he sees a terror beyond the apparent beauty. "Gifted with the high perception, I lack the low, enjoying power; damned, most subtly and most malignantly! damned in the midst of Paradise!"

I claim no such morbid high perception as Ahab's, then or now, claim only that it took me twenty years to see the intimate connection between death and beauty. Having established the connection, I still do not know what to do with it, but twenty years ago, all I recognized was contrast, paradox, and nowhere more than on the atoll of Ulithi.

We had moved there suddenly, inexplicably, and at such a bad time that we moved for twenty-four hours through a typhoon. I thought it was great. The wind blew so hard and steadily that the waves could not form. Any water drawn into a peak was quickly topped by the wind; the surface of the ocean looked like a desert with long lines of drifting sand, the scud from the waves. And the rain, the torrents, dampened the wave motion. We moved levelly all day and night in the midst of a howling wilderness.

So Ulithi was placid and lovely beyond words. The central lagoon, large enough to be a small ocean itself, large enough to shelter hundreds of ships, was circled by a dozen atolls, each a mile or so long, at most a hundred yards wide. Outside the atolls the ocean broke in thunderous claps on the coral reefs; inside, the water lay like a mill pond. When we arrived and anchored, we crowded the forward deck to study through the long glass an island with honest-to-God coconut palms and grass huts and tiny dark natives who may or may not have been nude—there was much debate on the subject. All day we watched. It was Sunday, April 1, 1945, the day of the invasion of Okinawa. We were privy to the knowledge of that terrible, bloody siege, yet the radio that day said not a word. We paced the decks, back and forth, looking at Paradise.

That night we watched the sunset. Perhaps a dozen rain squalls had developed all around the compass; the light on each one varied. Long after the sun had set, the entire crew lazed about the deck in purple shadow while the light on thunderheads grew a brighter gold. We cursed the long lingering light because it delayed our movies.

Next to the off-limits island of natives, tied to it by a submerged reef (like a pathway), was one of the recreation islands; it was segregated, of course, with enlisted men at one end and officers at the other. Our enlisted men rigged for the officers a canvas awning stretched between palm trees. They constructed picnic tables and dug a barbecue pit, and roaring parties were held there with beef cooked black on skewers, black outside and red inside. (I saw there an officer from another ship go off by himself, produce a book, and read. I maneuvered until I could see that he read Dante.)

But the islands, so beautiful from a distance, were disappointing. There were flies, sand fleas, the rank smell of rotting coconuts, a breezeless heat, and the sand was a dirty gray. So we swam all the time in the lagoon or crossed to the ocean side and waded cautiously on the reef. The size of the world shifted to sea anemones and sea urchins, great spiny things or delicate stringlike white worms, and an occasional spotted moray eel. We searched for shells, filling beer cans with cats-eyes with which to make bracelets to send home.

One of our chiefs went off swimming by himself and was drowned. Some said he had tried to wade the path to the native island.

Then the ships came back from Okinawa, and we were busy again. I remember one destroyer tied alongside us. A kamikaze plane had smashed into its engine room. Luckily only a wing-tip bomb had exploded and shattered the superstructure, killing I don't know how many. We asked for volunteers to help clean up the engine room; the Japanese pilot was still in there, of course, melted into the machinery. Someone found his wallet and took it around the ship all day showing the paper bills and the single contraceptive.

Ensign Bray and I found on the beach a hermit crab in a snail shell and spent twenty-four hours taking a photograph of it, then rigging an enlarger so that we could come up with a ten-by-fourteen print of the crab's head, each eye now bigger than the crab had been.

At 0800, one morning, the radio carried the news of Roosevelt's death. There was a sudden shock, the sense of loss, of futility, of being very tired of the war. For the day, it seemed more real than what we were doing. Then, we didn't forget, but we put the matter aside, to be worried over later. Out there, one death more was nothing.

I would omit to tell what happened on deck watch one bright still noon, except that it stands in such contrast to a later similar episode. The deck watch in port was

manned by junior officers, naturally, and was little more than a message center at the head of the gangplank. "Now hear this, now hear this," one began on the PA, and then summoned a boat crew or something and then noted everything in a notebook (which the Executive Officer later edited into the ship's log). It was a position of little importance and much pomposity. Though the ship was temporarily under the command of a junior officer, he did nothing but stand around, all spic and spittle, for four hours at a turn. The idleness will help explain my hesitation and stupidity.

It was the noon hour, the decks were deserted. A seaman and I stood there, craving cigarettes. Soon we would take turns going below for a moment for a smoke. We looked off to the islands, to the lovely deceptive palm trees, to the white line of surf beyond the islands. We looked at the same somnolence of the other ships anchored near us, at the closest ship, a destroyer escort. *Idly,* we watched little figures suddenly begin to run around idiotically in the sunlight. (Count seconds, now, as you read; the timing is important.) Curiously, we looked to another ship, a freighter, and saw figures running there, too.

"Sir?" asked the seaman. "What do you suppose they're doing over there?"

I meditated. "Well, it looks to me like they're going to GQ."

"Oh?" he said.

"Bring me the binoculars."

This, too, took time.

I focused on the DE. Sure enough, I could see gun crews donning life jackets and putting on helmets.

"Sir?" asked the seaman. "Do you suppose it's a drill?"

"Well!" I answered, authoritatively. "You wouldn't think they'd both have a drill at the same time, now, would you? Especially during chow."

"Sir?" asked the seaman. "Don't you think maybe we ought to go to GQ, too?"

I *hesitated*. We'd had no word from the radio shack, the normal procedure. I stepped to our phone and dialed. No answer.

Still, I hesitated. The Captain was at chow, everybody was at chow. Did I dare take the responsibility for disturbing their meal?

"Sir, listen."

Then we could hear, distinctly, the distant honk-honk of the GQ alarms on other ships. I hung up the phone and checked a third ship with the binoculars. It, too. I stood there, *thinking*.

Finally, the phone rang.

"Deck," I answered.

"Condition red! *Jesus!* Where've you been?"

So I pushed the little lever that started our horns and general pandemonium.

How much time elapsed since I should have been bright enough to take *immediate* action? But I could not believe that the war could possibly touch *me*. It does not matter that it was, in fact, a false alarm that noon. The lives of a thousand men had depended on me, and I stood in a dream.

TRANSFER

〜〜〜〜〜〜〜〜〜

MY NEXT GQ came a month later, after I had been transferred. Some bastard in BuPers in Washington must have idly, in the process of filing a routine fitness report, noticed something about dry docks in my record (Boston! The woman in the fish factory!), or some idiot IBM machine shuffling cards—inexplicably, unaccountably, the wheels turned and I was picked. No, I wasn't picked, selected, I was shanghaied, accidentally sent to hell, expendable—impersonally, without concern—and nobody cared, and I had no choice, and there was nothing I could do about it but swear. So swear I did—and left on schedule.

The carpenters built me a large wooden box for my accumulated gear (the box caught up with me six months later), and I piled into it my whites, my raincoat, my bridge coat, watercolors, books, and going-away presents. One of my metalsmiths had made an ash tray from a cylinder of stainless steel and engraved on it my name and the ship's name and "Best Wishes." The incomparable Lieutenant Commander K—— invited me to his cabin for an illegal drink and presented me a pair of bookends, the Navy insignia cast in brass. (I have them on my desk today, and use the ash tray still after all these years.) But when the deck watch called the boat for me, no one was there to see me off, and no one should have been; but even so, it hurt. I was a castaway and expendable, replaceable—and it was a new feeling.

But I was not alone. The boat took me to the other end of Ulithi to a "floating hotel" where some hundreds of officers and men in transit were temporarily housed, "awaiting further transportation." Living conditions in this limbo were unmentionable, and thank God I got off within a week (if some yeoman on board had mislaid my papers, I would be there still), but while I was there, duties were assigned, a GQ station, and all the rest.

Thus, a general-quarters alarm one afternoon. I took my position at a hatchway with orders to clear the deck of all transients. Consider the hundreds of men loafing on the deck and then the sudden panic. I stood at the hatchway rather like a floorwalker at an escalator in a department store. "Careful. Watch your step. Move along quickly. Everybody below."

Everybody, but one stubborn sailor.

"Why do we have to go down there?"

"Orders. It's safer. Down below."

"What do you do?"

"I stay out here. Everybody else down."

"I'm not going down! If the ship is hit, they'll all be caught down there like rats in a trap. I'm not going down!"

I looked around wildly for support, but there was none. The ship's crew was at the guns, all pointed in the general direction of the Japanese-held island of Yap, and the awful blast of the alarm system gave point to the conversation. Ahab, faced with the obstinacy of Stubb, said to him simply, "Down, dog, and kennel." I must have yelled some-

thing equally obnoxious. The sailor was surprised. So was I.
Down he went, but stayed on the ladder so that his head
stuck out.

I was tremendously pleased with myself until suddenly
I had the greatest feeling of being alone and in danger myself! I was finally wide awake, and everything was real. I
wanted to say "My God, it's *me!*" but there was no point
in that, the sailor watching to see what I would do next.
So I waited. We all waited. In vain. No plane appeared in
the sky.

I would not record at random shifting impressions,
except that the war for me was like that, with moments of
awakening, with the sudden realization that I was alone and
in danger. None of this went into my letters home. I fal-
sified those, lest someone discover me in my agony. More
than agony, it was mortal terror. It stays with me throughout my life, needing nothing to jog the memory; and the
sequence, the desperate need for security, the fear of being
in transit, en route in the universe, is a natural consequence.

That mortal terror has a sound, the peculiar sound of
brass shells knocking against each other, clashing. My "further transportation" turned out to be on a merchant ship
bound south for Manus, and I was duly transferred on
board. But first the merchant ship had to unload a cargo of
ammunition (from where? Detroit? To where?). I was given
a cabin to myself, more like a cell, with a single round porthole looking to the bow and down into the open forward
hold. The ship's cranes labored day and night to bring up
out of the hold on wood platforms or in cargo nets enormous
seven-inch shells. The work was done by a crew of Seabees,
all colored. The ship's second officer stopped by to assure
me that we would be blown up any minute, for the crew
was insanely careless. The wood platforms would swing side-

ways until they tilted the huge shells into space. Glimmering, glistening, they cascaded down onto the steel deck—and rolled there like tenpins—and did not explode. Sticking my head out the porthole, I watched with horror. I could not bear to look and so sat on my bunk listening to that godawful sound and to the spaces between the sound. This went on for hours. When I could stand it no longer, I braced my head in my hands and sobbed. This too became unbearable, and so I fell asleep. It was that simple. But I never forgot—never.

That trip to Manus was only less hectic. The ship carried a young Merchant Marine officer as Gunnery Officer, and we quickly made friends. The rest of the crew were civilians, all idiots. The Captain was a Dutchman, rotund, unshaven, and drunk, inarticulately drunk morning, noon, and night. It was pathetic to watch him try to rise out of his deck chair in order to pee through the rail. I was shown him (he never knew I was on board) as one is shown a mental patient in an asylum. At night, the Gunnery Officer poured out all his complaints to me in choked whispers and then went up by the inanimate Captain in order to steal two bottles of beer from the case beside him. I crossed the equator at night, drinking warm beer, watching the stars.

It was a relief to reach Manus, to be assigned to a Quonset hut sleeping twenty or so officers "awaiting further transportation (mine came in a few days, a dawn plane ride to Hollandia). Manus was a vast complex of Army installations hacked out of the jungle, the Quonsets on the edge of a green world. At dusk there came out from the wall giant bats—fruit bats with a two-foot wingspread, heavy, barely able to fly, the awful wings laboring audibly against the night air. Below them, a thousand or so Army men trooped to an outdoor amphitheater to see the same movies we had seen on board ship weeks before. Back in the Quonset hut, after the movie, we talked and talked, late into the night.

On Manus, in the midst of futility, some soldier had set out flowering plants in front of his Quonset hut and edged the walk with rows of white shells, and painted on a sign these words:

> If I had sixpence,
> I'd take threepence
> And buy hyacinths
> For my soul.

HOLLANDIA

〰〰〰〰〰〰〰

THE PLANE LANDED in a field edged by
low mountains. Before we were allowed to exit, someone
came through the plane pumping an old-fashioned fly
spray, apparently to prevent the spread of insects from
Manus to New Guinea. It was the most ridiculous gesture
I have ever seen, for when the door was opened, insects
poured into the plane, carried in on an incredible wave of
hot air.

The air was sweet, but palpable with damp. I remember
standing beside the plane in the sunlight, bewildered to
see that the little effort of getting out of the plane had
raised enough sweat to drench my shirt and that nameless
insects had fastened on me. I could not believe such steamy
heat and commented about it to the enlisted man in the
airport office. "Oh, this day ain't so bad yet. I don't guess
it's much over ninety-two, ninety-four. Wait till it gets *hot*."
I did not have long to wait, and in the following weeks I too
learned to distinguish degrees of temperature without using
a thermometer and learned the delight of a day that didn't
quite reach ninety. The heat gave a sense of constant op-
pression; not simply enervation, but a constant omnipotent
presence to be resisted. Niceties of expression, good man-

ners, tidiness were trivialities in such an atmosphere of un-
deserved burden. The heat set the mood of the men, the
mode of living, and made the war seem very far away, made
plans for the future seem useless.

Surely the heat affected the way I first saw the dry dock
—as a long, low, floating garbage can. The ARD's, auxiliary
repair docks, were rather an engineering feat at the time,
for they were both big and movable. Our dry dock had been
towed out from the States to bring a repair yard to the innumerable small vessels that took part in the Pacific war.
One must imagine a very long U with each arm some twelve
feet wide and three hundred feet long. The whole dock
could be partially submerged so that a ship could be
brought inside the U; then a gate was closed at the open
end; the U became a box of water; the water was pumped
out, everything rose, and the ship was left high and dry,
ready for repair work, serviced by two cranes that straddled
the sides of the dock. The hollow walls under the cranes
contained the crew quarters, a crew of some one hundred
and twenty men. The three officers and two warrant officers
lived in the two-level superstructure at the closed end, the

end curved roughly to the shape of the bow of a ship. Along the starboard side of our dry dock floated a large barge and two smaller ones, the carpenter shop and storage. The whole affair had a cluttered air to it and looked more like a building than a ship, and more like a blank wall than a building. I can't think of a lower order of things afloat in the Navy— valuable, useful perhaps, but an object of scorn to all. The odor of garbage came from the barnacles scraped from the bottoms of ships. Dead barnacles plus heat: this was to be my home for a year!

In sum, it was worse than I had anticipated, and I must have emitted my own odor of surliness and pride when I came on board. Nor was I mollified to discover that I would have a room to myself, a room nearly twelve by twelve, room enough to pace in. I had observed that the dock was not "shipshape" (it needed painting badly) and certainly it was not going to be a "taut ship" (the casual dress of all hands made that evident). Then, before lunch, I was invited to meet not the Captain but the other officers over a glass of jungle juice! This shocked me, the enormous five-gallon glass bottle filled with grain alcohol leavened by a handful of raisins, and I choked on the vile stuff like a novice, to the

delight of all. "Oh, you just aren't acclimatized yet. You'll get used to it." And someone else, "I've been in this mother-fucking place a year now and I'm still trying to get acclimatized." And a third, "Here's to us all getting acclimatized all to hell."

I met the Skipper at lunch. He shook hands—"Howdy,

Marse Robert"—and passed around the bottle of atabrine
pills. These little yellow pills are a preventive of malaria;
taken daily, over a period of weeks, they dye one's skin and
urine yellow. They are a bitter pill; the trick is to get them
down into the throat without letting them touch the tongue,
or so I discovered later. The Skipper watched with glee as
I tried desperately to wash away the taste of my first atabrine. Thus I did not take to the Skipper for some time—
months, in fact.

That lunch ended with the rapid exodus of the other officers (to sack out, I discovered later), leaving the Skipper
and me to have our little chat. I asked about my duties. He
reached around to the buffet behind him and brought out
an acey-deucy board. "Why, Marse Robert, this is your duty,
to let me beat you at this here game after lunch every day,
after dinner every day, and after breakfast, and in between
times too, day after day. I give you the privilege of first roll.
Losers always roll first anyway, and I can tell you are just
not going to be a winner at this game. Proceed, sir, when
you are ready."

He did not beat me at acey-deucy every time, but he did
beat me regularly. He must have won nine hundred and
fifty out of every thousand games. I could never figure out
why. I rapidly became adept, moving the counters to the
throw of the dice without having to count out each of the
spaces moved; I built up my defense to match his; I even
shook the dice cup as he did; but he consistently turned up
more often than I the one-and-two, acey-deucy, with the
bonus move of twenty-four spaces plus a second roll of the
dice. Within the month, we played for money, for pennies
at first. When I balked one day at paying a total, the Skipper
took my credit. When he left, I owed him four million dollars, and he took with him my IOU to that effect.

I was the Skipper's playmate. A Southerner, he teased
me unmercifully about my name ("Naow, just how is it you
know that Rubbet-E-Lee is really your great-great-great-

great—no? Three greats? Not four? Great-great-great-uncle
—*who* fed you that line?"). He was from Texas (he claimed
to have been a sheriff and in the pursuit of duty, he had, he
said, killed a "Nee-gra"), but he had spent most of his life
in the Merchant Marine, traveling around the world. He
had a million stories to tell and for a time conceived the idea
of my ghost-writing his autobiography, so that he talked
steadily while we played our acey-deucy. I believed little of
what he said (walking across the Sahara, for God's sake?)
and remember less. When the Skipper realized how easily
I was shocked, he shifted to dirty stories such that now nothing can shock me. ("Liverpool Sal was the dirtiest woman
I've ever seen. She had only one clean place on her, her right
tit, and to get that clean, I'd had to suck all night.") When
this tired him, he proposed a hunting expedition or a trip
to the Officers Club (Quonset huts)—and I was his com-
panion. We were anathema to each other and so got along
famously.

However, I found him out in his true character. A Bap-
tist chaplain came on board one afternoon. Probably he was
from some outfit on shore and came at the Skipper's invitation; but I like to think of him as a true itinerant, de-
scendant of the circuit riders; I imagine him as appearing
from nowhere, attached to no outfit but Jesus. A robust,
chunky, graying, cheerful man, he set up shop under an
awning out on deck, using a typewriter table for his altar
and hanging on the bulkhead behind it a large American
flag and in front of the flag a framed lithograph, a colored
head of Jesus. He brought along a stack of hymn books, and
after the Skipper had ordered up to the service every last
man on board, including the heathen officers, the preacher
passed out the books and lined out the hymns. An initial
reluctance on the part of the crew was soon overcome in
the wave of nostalgia at remembered tunes, and all sang
out the mournful words with good will. When the congre-
gation had been suitably warmed, the chaplain closed his

eyes, threw back his head, and invoked Jesus to come visit
with us all. The prayer merged gradually into the sermon,
such a hell-fire sermon as I had not heard since my child-
hood, on and on, his voice rising to an anguished shout, his
shirt soaked through with sweat, his hands and arms describ-
ing torment, and then dropping back into a sobbing prayer,
into invitation.

"Is there, O Lord, some poor sinner here today who wants
to come now into the arms of Jesus and be comforted? O
Lord, is there some poor suffering soul who will come up to
this altar this day and be saved, saved for all of eternity? Let
us all pray to liberate that poor sailor from his fear of dam-
nation, pray that he can see Jesus as I can here beside me,
right here, and come to Him and rest in His arms."

No one stirred. The chaplain labored for five minutes
more, but none of us—were we all lost?—would come forward to testify to his salvation.

Later, the Skipper reproached me for not accepting the
invitation, and I countered by saying that the Captain
should have gone first to set the example. "Oh, I've *been*
saved," he said, "half a dozen times."

I took this answer as typical until I saw the photograph
he had had taken of himself standing with the chaplain.
Skipper grins self-consciously, but there is a real light in
his eyes—the unmistakable sign of a man who has been in
converse with his Lord.

But to my duties on this godforsaken craft. I was
the First Lieutenant; i.e., third in command after the Captain and his Executive Officer; the position was no great
honor, considering there were only three regular officers on
board. Next, I was Damage Control Officer, Chief Censor,
Supply Officer, Personnel Officer, in charge of the officers'
mess—I don't know what all, really, and can't think what
anybody else did, since I had so many titles. But I didn't

do much—none of us did. The Executive Officer was the
Docking Officer and had the rather delicate job of floating
a ship into the dock, centering it over the hidden haul and
keel blocks, and then adjusting the rates of the various
pumps so that the dock-and-ship rose up out of the water
all on an even keel. I tried it a couple of times, but after I
brought a tug in too fast and it nearly continued right on
through the superstructure, I thankfully turned the job
back to the Exec. Ships (boats, more precisely, a matter of
comparative size) came into dock once or twice a week; the
dirty work of scraping barnacles and repainting the hulls
was done by an Army crew from shore—colored, of course.
So even our own crew had little to do but take care of the
dock itself. My own work kept me occupied at the most two
hours a day; the acey-deucy games took as much time or
more. Two hours of work, two hours of games, two hours at
the movie each night, ten hours in the sack—I had eight
free hours a day for a *year*. And of course the problem was
to use up that time, profitably or not profitably, at least to
keep busy enough so one didn't go crazy, stark raving mad,
as one of our crew members did.

You might think: What a grand opportunity! One could
read the Bible or all of Shakespeare! Write a book! Design
a Utopia! Spend weeks in the carpenter shop or in the
darkroom (makeshift it was, but we had one)! Study marine
biology! Learn electrical engineering! What could one *not*
do! I had some such ideas, I must admit, and I look back
on them in some bitterness, remembering that the free time
came in midday, that there was never any privacy, that it
was always noisy, that it was never cool. I could not close my
door and my portholes because the steel room would quickly
turn into an oven. At night, the movie screen hung right
outside my door; I could not even leave a light on during
the movie. So the hours melted away, the days, the weeks,
the opportunity to learn and to do—most of it vanished in
idleness or homesickness or fretfulness.

But perhaps it was not such a waste after all, for there were things to do outside oneself, adventures such as the trip inland by jeep to hunt wild boar or, better still, the trips by boat east along the coast to visit native villages. One day— nothing climactic happened, or anything to make it into a story—but the one day in its entirety, in its total effect, turned out to be so unsettling I still cannot accommodate it in my thoughts.

The deck watch roused us at 0445 while it was still dark—the Skipper, one of the warrant officers, half a dozen seamen, myself—and we left in the LCM when there was just light enough to see the water, for we had been told by one of the men who had been there before that it was a four-and-a-half-hour trip. The coxswain had a difficult job keeping in close enough to shore to avoid the deep ocean swells, but not so close that we would be caught in the breakers and swept onto some invisible reef. Constantly he kept trying the open sea, but the boat rocked so violently he had to head into shore and out again, in and out. The smell of gasoline, the nausea was frightful, and I was not the only one who purged himself over the side. After an hour or so, with the sun up, the ocean seemed calmer, the boat steadier (but I was aware of our utter reliance on the two engines of the LCM).

The early morning was pleasant, the breeze created by our motion keeping us cool. For a time we could see the low mountains behind the shoreline; a wisp of cloud draped along the peaks. Then we shifted course and saw only the jungle, like a dark wall, and to the left the deep blue of the sea. We were beautifully isolated and seemingly without motion. Suddenly we were in a herd of porpoises. They arched out of the water, gray, glistening, to look at us, and curved back in and plummeted deep out of sight. They burst into the air again and again and back into the water, like the sweep of a hand on harp strings, over and over. Passing the porpoises, we watched more closely, and after a time someone spotted a sea turtle just under the surface of the water. The coxswain cut the engines, and we drifted alongside. It was a monstrous thing, big as a table, with massive flippers and a reptilian head. We got too close, and the turtle sank out of sight. Later, we saw sharks ("Hey, look, look! My God, it's just like the movies!"); rather, we saw the upright fins in the murky water where a river emptied into the sea. Then there was a point of land, which we rounded, into a quiet lagoon, to a landing, and we were there.

I remember most, I think, the sudden silence when the engines were still; and the height of the trees, the long slender trunks wrapped in vines; and the sudden surge of heat out of the trees; and the sweet smell. We found a path into the jungle and advanced with caution, ill at ease, though the officers had pistols and two of the men carried rifles. Our man who had been there reported the natives were absolutely friendly ("How do you know they aren't headhunters, hey? Did 'ja ask 'em?"), but when a bird cried out suddenly, we all panicked. In another moment, we felt ridiculous, for a native came down the path to greet us.

It was a tiny, wizened old man. He called out something between "Hi" and "Hello" and hobbled up to us, grinning like a mad man. He must have been about four feet six, nude except for a loincloth suspended under his distended belly. He had thongs tied just above his biceps and a mesh bag slung over his left shoulder. He had scanty, black bushy hair and a white fringe of beard on his chin. His eyes were so gentle, so soft, so human, one had to turn away from his comprehending stare. He grinned, shook hands, drooled orange betel-nut juice out of his orange mouth, and led us to the village.

The village, surrounded by handsome palm trees, was no more than twenty houses in a clearing with a street of sorts, a sandy level place. Each house was square with a high pyramidical roof of thatch. The floor was raised five feet from the ground on poles, and the space underneath was used for storage. But this does not indicate the pleasant yellow color, the noise of birds and barking dogs, a sudden sense of enchantment. It was much later that I looked carefully for some sign of civilization, some metal, and saw only a ten-gallon pail and planed boards made into steps to one house. These were obviously recent gifts from visiting Navy personnel, like the white undershirts and the khaki shorts worn by some of the men.

When we first entered the clearing, we saw only the men; the women and children stayed in the houses or in the shadows underneath. Soon, however, the children came out, bone-naked, although the girls wore earrings. Both boys and girls had their heads shaved except for a ridge down the middle. Then the women. They wore low on their stomachs a sort of wraparound made of bark cloth. Their bellies bulged, and their bared pendant breasts hung sideways. The women were fuzzy-headed and dark. Several of them kept up a constant scratching, and when they dared to come closer we saw that their bodies were covered with some kind of loathsome skin disease, a ringworm perhaps, decorating with oozing circles every square inch of their

bodies—forearms, faces, breasts, and hands. One woman
wore a bracelet made of a bent toothbrush.

Our business, however, was with the men, who brought
out what they had to sell: shells, bows and arrows, models
of outrigger canoes, Japanese coins, spears, bananas, a dead
bird of paradise, a fly switch of emu feathers. They wanted
cloth ("lap lap") for these, but were content to trade for the
cigarettes we had brought. (Our cigarettes were always in
plentiful supply and always fresh, each carton having been
coated with paraffin; a carton of two hundred cigarettes cost
us just fifty cents in the ship's store). So we began to trade.

"Nice," I said to a man holding a woven basket of shells
(I wanted the basket). "How much?"

"Two lap laps," he answered promptly.

"No got," I said.

He laughed and went away and came back, his price
changed to "four cigarette" (four packs).

So it went. There is some sad economic truth in this interchange, but I disregard it.

I had some vague memory of having seen in the Field Museum in Chicago masks and carvings from New Guinea. These were what I looked for and did not find; nevertheless, I was very pleased with two utilitarian objects, an empty coconut and a comb. The coconut was used as a box, its entire surface carved into geometric designs, the incised lines made white with lime. The comb was a segment of bamboo, with fourteen tines something like a fork. On the handle was this design:

Is it a pelican? Do the slant lines indicate flight? Purposefully or accidentally?

But it was time to go home with our loot. The women lined up for a photograph. One of our men made the gestures of intercourse to learn their word for it ("mog mog"), and the women laughed, and the children laughed to see them laugh. We took photographs of everyone, even the one dour, warlike man who had not participated in the trading or even greeted us. Our old man posed under the outstretched arm of the skipper to show his height or lack of it. Everybody accepted one last cigarette, and off we went.

The whole innocent expedition disturbed me inordi-

nately, and I was several years finding out why. My first thought was that we were, with our civilization, contaminating the natives of New Guinea. I got the word "contaminating" straight from Margaret Mead. In our senior year at college, my roommates and I went to hear her lecture, and, on a dare, I approached her afterward and asked if she would come to our apartment for coffee. None of us were anthropologists, but Miss Mead didn't care. We got two more hours of lecture and good talk; and I can remember her warning that primitive peoples would disappear from the world in another hundred years. One of the side-effects of the Pacific war, she went on, was the contamination of every tribe in the Pacific. And yes, I can vouch for that now, but I could not get very disturbed about it, preferring sanitation to carved birds.

Although, of course, I treasure the bird on the comb—as I do the photographs of the women's breasts and even the enlargement we made of the one dour man, glaring at the camera. After the war, I bought a book on the art of the Pacific, and searched in it for something like my souvenirs. I did not find them, but I read enough to make me even more curious. For instance, I learned that spiritual beings stay in a secret clubhouse and make the masks and carvings used for ceremonies; that the male novices on coming of age have to be told that there are in fact no spiritual beings, that it is the men themselves who make the masks; the women and children are never told this; the men alone know that there is no god. And so on. Therefore I went back to the Field Museum, to the South Pacific room at the east end of the basement, so remote and at the time such a jumble of poorly lighted cases that no one much came there, not even a guard. I took along a drawing board, charcoal and pastels, and a folding stool, and roamed from one case to the next until I found something simple enough to sketch—so that by concentrating on one item at a time, I might sort out the confusion of bowls, utensils, drums, weapons, chairs, masks,

and gods—as if there were some secret in them. And there
was, of course. There were the gods made out of tree-fern
trunks, more than life-size, one enormous head standing
on top of another, with great blank eyes; or the little standing statues with their ornate penises; or the face masks,
more animal than human, the eyes outlined in repeating
stripes, in greens, pinks, blue; the men become gods, masks
made to terrify the beholder, all wild, staring. These I
sketched and rubbed color onto the paper with my finger
tips, but like the men who made the masks, I knew deep
down there were no gods.

I snapped the picture of the dour man and later in the
darkroom watched under the red light as the enlargement
developed (rubbing the paper with my finger tips). Here
is the man I saw: the hard muscles of his chest, the thong
tied above his biceps, a vein distended on his arm and
another jagged on his forehead, the bushy hair, the flattened
nose, the points of spears showing beside him, but mostly
the eyes, deep-set, wary, distrustful, and the whole proud
face glassed in the sunlight.

Over the years the face, the man, the savage in this entire
context stares at me.

Some of our men went back down the coast on an
expedition to salvage a boat, or some such pretext. One of
them boasted on his return that he had slept with the native
women. He and two others got malaria, and the stories that
came back to us from sick bay ashore were frightening. One
of the men came close to death: last rites, his heart stopped,
miraculously revived, and such spasms he tore gashes in his
own tongue; and all three of them were sent back to the
States with permanent disabilities. The rest of us took our
atabrine.

The rains came in daily torrents, and steam rose from the
deck. Some of the men developed funguses—raw skin

wounds that would not heal, the flesh putrefying. It was the weather, perhaps, or our diet. Our food supplies deteriorated. From the States came the insipid Spam and the dehydrated potatoes that our cooks turned into a sodden gray mush with a vile taste. From Australia came gallon cans of rancid butter and lamb with its variants of mutton, sheep, and ram—the meat tough, gray as the potatoes, and equally vile. No fresh fruit or vegetables. Dehydrated milk, coffee from the raw beans that had been in our damp holds for two years. And no expectation of any improvement.

Hence the grudge fights. Whenever Warrant Officer D—— spotted two men in daily quarrels he arranged a formal fight for them in the cleared space on the carpenter's barge alongside. Only the Captain knew nothing of this. The rest of us jammed down there late at night to watch the men slug it out with boxing gloves—to exhaustion, for D—— was the referee and a highly partial one, urging on the strongest man, never calling time when the underdog was hurt, blinded with blood.

The Captain went on a rampage. The dock must be cleaned. Now. Inspection. "My God," he'd say, "look at this crap hole. No movies, no shore leave until this place is painted every inch." And then he acquired a dog from somewhere, a black, vicious, yapping asshole of a dog, and he forgot the inspection in his joy at the companionship of the dog, and we believed he taught the dog to bark at any movement on deck, and he constantly called the deck watch to come and clean up the dog's mess, so that there was talk of throwing the dog overboard. Restless again, the Skipper took me down to inspect the kitchen late one night, even to the point of pulling out the splatter boards behind the stoves. We uncovered cockroachs, thousands on thousands of them. Next day the food tasted of kerosene spray.

We—the officers, that is—got some fresh food, specifically, eight eggs, which the Exec got from a ship in the bay, trading some hundred dollars' worth of equipment for the eight

eggs. We five (including the two warrant officers) spent a
jovial evening anticipating breakfast, discussing how the
eggs were to be cooked, how divided. But in the morning
our colored boy reported tearfully that in the night someone had smashed the eggs on the galley floor. Skipper flew
into a black rage, barking out orders. All hands on deck,
and in an hour the guilty man found—drunk? insane?—
and his gear was packed and he was sent ashore to sick bay
"for observation," never to return.

While it rained each afternoon, it was less hot, and I
could sack out in my room, sleep or read. But the Captain
could not sleep, and he ordered me up to his room. "Marse
Robert, even my dog could beat you at acey-deucy. Y'all
got to have some more practice now.

On August 7, 1945, at about 1300 (Skipper and I
were playing acey-deucy), we heard about Hiroshima. On
the 15th (the 14th in the States), the war was over. To most
servicemen it was the latter event that seemed more significant at the time and in that place. Who, after all, twenty
years later, can really comprehend the atomic bomb?

Though I have not mentioned it, we followed assiduously
the details of the war via news broadcasts, weekly newsreels
put out by the Armed Forces, and magazines (*Time, News-
week,* and the *New Yorker,* in miniature lightweight edi-
tions, were flown overseas and reached us without much
delay). The war for us was solely a Pacific war. The war in
Europe ended? Good, because it meant more matériel for
the endless job of island-hopping, for the big invasion of
Japan that would take no one knew how many years. We
were aware of the distances and the problems involved; but
it was by hearsay, for we were as remote from the action as
were my parents in Iowa; and thus we were only half listening to the radio in the wardroom when the bombing of

Hiroshima was announced. Doomsday will come equally
without anticipation or preparation or comprehension.

We were quick to realize that the bomb meant the end
of *our* war, and we rejoiced. *Matériel* had triumphed. Evil
had been put down by the force of arms. Someone on our
dry dock in the course of that first day developed a peace
plan: disarm the Japs, start at the north end of Japan, kill
all the men, and send over all our Negro men to take care
of the women. But such talk was idle. The Captain allowed
the men to drink beer on the carpenter barge, and there
we waited, listening to the short-wave, to the polyglot lan-
guages whose only comprehensible words were "atomic
bomb." One broadcast relayed from Hong Kong was in
English, and I jotted down these words: "The Americans
are now able to destroy all civilization; therefore the Americans must be destroyed. If a million men invade our home-
land, a million men will be killed. As long as we keep our
spiritual soul they cannot kill us. The atomic bomb destroyed a city, many churches and schools and shrines, and
killed uncounted civilians." This was followed by mandolin
music.

That night, I could not sleep. My private reactions began
as those of an engineer intrigued with the announcement
that the bomb was two thousand times more powerful than
the 11.2-ton bomb used in Europe. I played with figures
until I came up with one thousand B-29's capable of de-
stroying in one day two hundred and twenty areas the size
of Manhattan. I was quick to see that navies had become
useless, and armies, and that no bomb protection was possible; and there would not have to be a physical invasion
of Japan; and I went on to visualize the bombs leveling a
road through the Himalayas or dredging in a day a canal
across Panama.

Still, I could not sleep. I recalled having read Stephen
Vincent Benét's poem "Nightmare for Future Reference,"
dating from about 1938, in which he predicted a war that

ended abruptly because the women of the entire world had
become unable to produce children. I recalled the illustra-
tion of Hendrik van Loon illustrating I don't know what,
but the entire human race was packed into one giant box
balanced on a mountain peak until someone's pet dachs-
hund nudged the box and ended it all. No one, I think,
could comprehend the scale of the catastrophe, certainly
not the little, myopic, inarticulate man in the White House
who ordered Nagasaki on top of Hiroshima while he con-
demned the bestiality of the Nazis.

I wrote home that night that the bomb was the most important event in history since the coming of Jesus Christ,
that mankind could destroy itself, that nationalism would
have to be forefeited in the face of the power to obliterate,
and so on. I do not claim any special sensitivity or guilt or
rage, but I know that my thoughts for twenty years have
been governed by the event of that one August day and that
I am still no closer to an accommodation of that monstrous
revelation.

It helps, I believe, to see the bomb in terms of that marvelous machine of Yves Tanguey that destroyed itself in
the garden of the Museum of Modern Art. This assemblage
of bicycle wheels and electric motors, whistles, smoke pots,
rockets, and colored lights was purposely designed to whir
magnificently and then independently to tear itself to
pieces. It did not quite succeed. Instead, it spawned, I pre-
sume, the LSD generation and the God-is-dead movement,
but it makes a fine picture of the atomic bomb, or, as we
must call it now, the hydrogen bomb.

There was, you see, in the shock of knowledge the chance
to end all the waste and hierarchy, the idle killing and the
meaningless motion. That urge turned my college roommate Web into a nuclear physicist (and pacifist) and my
other roommate Shep into a landscape architect, and myself
into a professor.

But, as I said, the second event—the peace—dominated

our thoughts. We had all been in the war too long and seen too much that we could not comprehend. The bomb meant simply to a generation that we could go home, and that ended our moral concern. The colored boy who did my room woke me up on Sunday morning, August 12, to tell me gleefully that the war had ended. It had not, but on Wednesday, August 15, 1945, at 0800, New Guinea time, the official announcement did come through. Every ship in the harbor ran up its signal flags; bells, whistles, sirens went off; and that night, with every person in Hollandia drunk, the ships began firing their small guns. We had some difficulty deciding who was Gunnery Officer on the dry dock and then we realized nobody on board knew how to operate our 40mm. gun; so we contented ourselves with firing off all the Very pistols and watching the tracer bullets from other ships. Then some son of a bitch shot low right over us, and we had to scatter. The radio reported that three men in Okinawa, celebrating, were killed.

September 1945-
May 1946

NORTHWARD

~~~~~~~~~~~~~~~~~~~~~~~~~~~~~~~~

WE HAVE ORDERS to leave New Guinea. Nobody is sorry. Any place we go will be closer to home than Hollandia. Any motion is better than none. With unseemly haste we take into the dock our two pontoon barges and the carpenter's barge and pump out the well of the dock. The barges have been in the water so long their bottoms are hoary with barnacles, algae, seaweed. These attract fish, and when the barges are moved, the fish move. When the water drains out from under the barges, we can see the fish on the floor of the dock, thousands of tiny tropical fish in bright blue, red, or emerald green, some in stripes of black, yellow, and white. Their color fades quickly.

Then we wait a maddening week until an ocean-going tug arrives to tow us to the Philippines. Two small tugs assist in getting us out of our mooring. We have five anchors to reel in with winches. It takes five hours. One winch breaks under the strain and a wheel two feet in diameter shoots off into the bay, nearly taking my leg with it. Adrift, the dock is unwieldy, to say the least. Every ship in the harbor is threatened by us when the wind catches us broadside. We lurch out between coral reefs and are free.

The tug pays out to us a two-inch cable some three or four hundred yards long. Almost imperceptibly, the nearby hills begin to move. There is a deathly quiet in our wheelhouse, for of course we have no engines, and the tug's engine is too far away to hear. We have to set our rudders to counteract any side wind, and man the wheelhouse with Montana, Greer, Kuznet, and Pellegati taking turns at the wheel, but that's all. Each officer has to sit in the wheelhouse four hours on and eight hours off, but no navigation is required. And there are no GQ's. And the Captain takes his turn at the watch so that when he's off duty he's sleepy and not meddlesome. Hours later, at sundown, the hills of New Guinea are noticeably smaller, but they are still there! Our speed reaches about five knots. We will average only one hundred and twenty land miles every twenty-four hours, and we have two thousands miles to go! But it is motion, and we are happy beyond words.

Alfred's Navy Rules.

1. Avoid enthusiasm. It doesn't pay.

2. Let others do the thing. Then it won't be your fault.

3. If everybody minded his own business there'd be no trouble. Do what you're told to do if you have to, but don't let it influence you. Remember, it's none of your business.

4. People will always be trying to make you do something you don't want to do. Let on you don't hear them.

In the last hours before daybreak the stars were especially bright. They delineated the distant islands to port and starboard. The Sulu Sea was so calm the stars flicked in the water. Ahead, the lights of the tug were as steady as the stars in the sky. Greer and I arched our cigarettes over the side.

Greer was eighteen, a second-class seaman from an Indiana farm. He said, with a naive admiration, almost with a personal pride, "Lookit all the stars."

But he was not young enough to be satisfied with such contentment and after a time he asked which was the North Star. We traced out the line from the bowl of the Great Dipper and found the North Star just over the tug, where it ought to be, for our course is ooo. "How about that?" said Greer, marveling at the precision.

Then we located Orion. Greer had never heard of Orion and he could not be persuaded that it really looked like the figure of a warrior, except he would grant me the belt and the sword.

"Now," I said, "the three stars of the sword. Notice anything about one of them?"

"Which one? What about it?"

"No, you tell me."

"Oh." He studied them awhile. "It's the middle one. It's hazy."

"Right," I said and waited.

He said at last, "Why?"

My satisfaction was sweet. "It's a nebula," I said.

"What's that?" he asked suspiciously.

As I explained, it became clear that the boy had never heard of a nebula. I could sense his obedience—whatever an officer told him must be right—and his doubt, his reluctance to think of such an enormity.

He got binoculars to check Orion.

"It's hazy, all right."

"There are more stars there than there are here. There are nebulae the human eye can't see without a telescope. There are dozens, hundreds of nebulae in the sky . . ." And on I went, with poor Greer bewildered by this new knowledge and always thereafter unable to see simply stars.

I would not have him ignorant of the force of the universe, though he soon went back into the wheelhouse and turned on the short-wave radio, and I could hear the song "Shoo, shoo, baby." I stayed outside to watch the dawn.

The music did not disturb my contentment. The two weeks, more than two weeks, at sea had been like a shucking off of evils, a reduction, a return to the simplicities of water, sky, and wind. I had been able to recapture a sense of aloneness, to make a kind of place of my own. We were as children again, venturing into a world where there was no harm. Each snail-paced dreamlike day revealed new wonders: the smell of spices on the wind; a bos'n bird motionless in the sky; seven waterspouts rimming the horizon; a Filipino sailboat moving faster than we did; the coolness of the wind; and then the Basilan Strait where the tug could make no headway for seven hours against the wind, while the dock rolled back and forth in a destructive urge, throwing out anything not battened down; Zamboanga ("Oh, the monkeys have no tails in Zamboanga!"), where we saw only the lights at night, but we were satisfied; and then the rain squalls, and the palm trees, and a PBY making a pass over us; and Greer showing Orion to Pellegati who steadfastly refused to see any nebular haze.

MARIVELES

~~~~~~~~~~~~~~~~~~~~~~~~~~

I WENT ASHORE FIRST, to talk with the Shore Patrol before our liberty party landed. My guide I will call Jones.

"Hell, I been in Mar'veles too long. When did we retake Manila? May, was it? May. This is September, isn't it? I been in this jerkwater town it must be four, five months. I haven't been ashore for I don't know, I can't remember how long. But they just built the Blue Goose. I gotta see that. Tell your bos'n to—hey, sailor, head over there. Got it? That's Corregidor behind us. This is Bataan. This is where the Death March started. It used to be a quarantine station. That was a federal building. Sailor, you just go back and wait for the liberty party, at what time? What the hell time is 1900? Seven o'clock? I'll have the lieutenant back here by then. Understand? Shove off, now. Where was I? Well, they bombed it, then we bombed it, then before Corregidor went the whole army surrendered here, and then they walked them around the bay. Walk, hell. We got the bastard, though, General Somebody. We're going to shoot him. Now the people are coming back. They live in the shacks down there. This part's Army. Your dock's assigned to the Army, you know that? If you ask me, I think the Army's using this as a secret base to run guns over to Chiang Kai-shek, you know? You're gonna get the damnedest boats in that dock— nobody'll answer questions. Let's go find the mayor and get a drink."

The mountain behind the town reared up in soft curves to the clouds. Its slopes were jungle, and the town sat on a fringe of beach, just where the hills began, in a curve backed by impenetrable green. A muddy creek separated the Army part of the town from the Filipino. We headed left, to the Army tents clustered around the federal building. It was a fine building of concrete, with a two-story arch at the main entrance, a Greek pediment, and arched galleries on each side. There was little left to it but the façade, and it was half destroyed, smudged black from fire. The building had no roof. Inside, a few rooms remained, the tiled floors coated with mud. In one room was an Army doctor; in another, Army radio; in another, children at school. The mayor wasn't there.

"Correction. José was mayor for seventeen years, but they got enough people back to have an election, and he's out. He must be down at his club."

A boy ran ahead of us down the dirt road, and soon José Sorreál hurried out to greet us, a charming elderly man in a straw hat, horn-rimmed glasses, a clean neat shirt (blue, worn like pajama tops), baggy trousers, and tennis shoes. The advent of one hundred more servicemen, fifty of them that very night, was indeed good news. The Blue Goose had been finished just in time. José took us in and boasted that his room had the only dance floor in town and a raised al- cove at one end for an orchestra of six. "Seex. Seex men." There was a bar at the other end and tables to the south with a view of the bay and of Corregidor beyond.

Jones ordered a pint of Scotch, and José apologetically

charged us the normal price of ten pesos, or five dollars. It was a whiskey made in Manila, described as "Black Label Scotch Whiskey of Great Age." I can't describe the dreadful taste. We drank it straight, not trusting the water, and quickly, for maximum effect.

José introduced us to his nephew Domine, age sixteen, the bartender; then to a girl Ida; and then to his three hostesses, Rosie, Mary, and Doree, all younger than Domine. José explained that his girls would dance with the guests, but if they wanted pom-pom, they would have to go somewhere else.

"Let's take a look at the pom-pom, Lieutenant. Hell, ain't you supposed to inspect the recreation facilities?"

José escorted us down the dirt road to a shack just across a small bridge, one of two cat houses. The shack was raised on stilts above the mud; its walls were of bamboo, the roof a combination of thatch and corrugated sheet metal. We were met by an Army lieutenant just coming out from his twice-weekly inspection, accompanied by the manager (a boy of about twenty in a silk shirt and khaki pants) and the two girls, some eighteen years old, in neat silk dresses and wooden sandals. The lieutenant assured us they were clean, and the price, ten pesos, was standard. (He claimed they could make three hundred pesos a night.) The girls flashed their gold teeth at us and touched us.

Jones elected to go in and I to stay out. José and I sat on the rail of the bridge and waited. The manager stood at the head of the stairs and peered through the curtain, singing out from time to time in Tagalog.

José translated. "He says Jones is very slow. He is an old man. He says he is too drunk."

We waited, watching three tiny boys play on the bridge, shooting at each other, "bam bam," with wooden guns. An Army private went past, a rifle slung over his shoulder; he

saluted, said hello, and grinned, for he was leading on a chain a gray monkey, which walked erect on its hind legs. After that, a man went by balancing on his head long green palm fronds, which he would use on the roof of his house. Three old women passed by, balancing five-gallon tins of water on their heads; they said hello to José, turning their heads slightly; the water spilled and dripped on their dresses and showed their breasts. A pretty girl went by next, balancing on her head a flat tray piled with grain; she walked quickly, her sandals slapping the bridge; she did not need to use her hands to balance the tray until she said hello, and then she put up one hand to steady it. Later, a boy came by on the back of a wet black water buffalo.

When Jones came out, unsteadily, he bragged that he felt like a young man again. "But I'll sure as hell worry for the next three weeks. Come on, José, sell us another pint."

In spite of my protests, we went back to the Blue Goose and shared another pint of Scotch. This time José made us a present of half a dozen red bananas, which we ate with the Scotch. Presently, the boys of the orchestra came in and began to play. The three hostesses, dressed in starched cotton dresses, sat with us and asked questions. "How much pesos we need to go to the States? When you think we can get on a sheep?"

It was dusk when we left, and things were roaring in my head. The liberty party met us halfway back to the wharf, and I had sense enough to say nothing, just wave them on. Jones leaned toward them and with motionless dignity vomited up his Scotch and bananas. They all cheered.

It is difficult to reconstruct what happened at the Blue Goose later that night. Redheaded, pugnacious, drunken Smith (I shall call him) challenged a number of people to a fight, was led out to the beach and persuaded to forget about fighting, shook hands with everyone, and then swung. It started a free-for-all. Even Smith agreed that he had started it. When he was knocked down, however, some exuberant soul kicked him in the teeth.

His lower gum was split, his jawbone fractured, two teeth were knocked out, and three more would have to be pulled. In fact, he had to be sent to a hospital at Manila, and after the next day we never saw him again.

He came in to borrow twenty-five dollars from me and spoke about his troubles, each word causing him pain.

"I hope I learned my lesson this time. Honest, sir, I should have known better. I've been in one fight when I got drunk, but I wasn't hurt much that time. It's in my family. My dad got to brawling so one night, my mother told my brother to knock him out. My brother he weighs two hundred pounds and he hit my dad up against a stove and nearly killed him. You'd think I would have learned."

In October, on Navy Day, we invited José Sorreál and a dozen others to bring their wives on board for movies. They were so neat, I had to remind myself that some of these people had spent over three years hiding out in the jungle surrounding Mount Mariveles, living in caves or in thatch huts, waiting for a time to return to their homes (no doubt some were collaborators who had lived in Manila, but I gathered that current social standing depended on the degree of one's independence). And I had seen their homes without a single modern convenience unless it were a kerosene lamp purchased at an exorbitant price on the Chinese market at Manila. But on board they came, the women as small and as pretty as dolls, magnificent in long bright dresses of blue or yellow with starched puffed sleeves, shy and giggling, and immaculately clean. We served them beer and sandwiches and then showed them movies: *The Fighting Lady,* about an aircraft carrier, and newsreels of the recapture of Manila, which created much excitement.

We did what we could to help the people of Mariveles. Jesus A. Zubiri, owner of the sailing vessel *Ligaya,* came the next week to ask us to do some welding on a winch, and then invited the Skipper and me to visit him and accept what we would: bananas, ginger root, tomatoes the size of grapes. We spent much time, too, with Chloe Roye, the father of three, owner of the Virginia Bar and teacher of the fifth and sixth grades. He looked about old enough to be my son, but looks meant nothing; who of us could conceive of his life in the last four years, in a cave, with his children? When the Japanese came in 1942, he realized he could not carry his typewriter with him, so he had packed it in grease in its case and buried it; four years later, though the case had rotted away, the typewriter was in perfect shape. Mr. Roye was delighted with our gift of seeds. He had been sent to Manila to buy seeds for the whole village and had found only a pound of peas. Skipper and I in New Guinea had planned a garden, ordered seeds from home, and these arrived just before we left; so we gave them to Mr. Roye.

Mr. Roye introduced us to Andres Balyrio, a Negrito, exactly four feet high. Andres was coal-black and carried a rifle. He was sixteen years old and married.

Mr. Roye explained that the Negritos lived in a village some three miles back in the mountains and that they had hated the Japs.

"But Andres, he's too young. Andres, you ever kill any Japs?"

"Yess!"

"How many?"

He pointed at his shoes. "Thees one!"

Andres hiked us back through bamboo groves to his village to meet his family, and I would say more about it except it's too fantastic to believe. No one in the village was more than four feet six inches high, all looking like children. They smoked our cigarettes by putting the lighted end *inside* their mouths. Surely the memory of this is not real nor, on our return trip, the iguana scuttling through the dry leaves under the bamboo.

Scene: The women of Mariveles washing their clothes in the stream, pounding them with sticks, draping them on bushes to dry while they washed themselves, modestly, with their dresses on, submerging, and then after, undoing their long black hair and combing it in the sunlight.

Scene: Some seven children being given a ride on a jeep, driving down the one street and back, squealing with delight.

The war seemed so remote and so unimportant—devastating, like a typhoon, perhaps, but no more than that. The life of the village, much more important than the life of an individual, had recovered.

"Dance with me, Meester Lee." It was Rosie, the child. I did my best but the top of her head came up only to my chest and if I bent close I got a whiff of the oil in her hair. Besides, she was not interested in anyone but herself. The villagers stood outside and watched through the windows. Rosie sang as she danced, "Whan they bee-geen the bee-geen, the or-chest-tra plaays—" When we finished, she flipped off to sit with one of the enlisted men. I was cornered by one of our seamen.

"That 'uns just a young kid. But that other one, boy, she's got it. She says—well, I know you could have her for nothin'. That Ida one. I was up with her the other night. It ain't like at the Bamboo Hut where they got them fucking pimps. No, this Ida she's got her own little shack, and you go in with her and nobody elst does."

He stopped long enough to drain his bottle of beer. Then he yelled, "Hey, Pop, get 'im a chair with a back on it, get this goddam stool outta here, get 'im something, you know, with a back on it."

He went off and came back with a bottle of beer for me

and with Ida. "There, I got ya fixed up. Remember what I said?" Then he left.

Ida wore a white dress, which went beautifully with her heavy black hair. Her fingernails were carefully lacquered. She wore great circles of gold in her pierced ears. She refused a drink, refused a cigarette, and sat without talking, looking only at me. Her face was beautiful; dark, with little crow's-feet at the corner of her eyes, a slight foreign twist of skin at her eyes, too. She smiled, lightly, and with a casual movement put her hand on mine. Very soon, our fingers were together.

"How old are you, Ida?"

"Oh, feefty. Feefty years old."

"Stop kidding. Tell me now. How old are you?"

"Twenty-seven."

"When were you born?"

"I was born 1918. Twenty-seven. See?"

"Are you married?"

"Yes—no. I was married. Not now."

"Did your husband—are you divorced?"

"What you mean?"

"Did your husband—die?"

"I don't know. The Japanese got him."

She tossed her head and looked away. After a time, she turned back, smiling. "How much pesos?"

"What?"

"How much pesos?"

The report from the Filipino patrol: "While we were on patrol on way to the Blue Goose Bar, we heard that there was a trouble among the sailors. Being town patrol we proceeded to that place. As we came inside, we found out that there was a hand to hand fight among the sailors. We determined to stop the trouble, but the sailors will not heed our orders, instead one of them grabbed me, sock me on the head, and throw me on the floor, while lying on the floor, some of them kicked me and even tried to get my night club. What I did, I crawled to the outside just to save me from the trouble. My two other companions were being socked by the sailors. I have seen that they even tried to get the carbine of the patrol. While I was outside resting for I feel dizzy, more sailors came and trouble again started outside. I have seen the sailors throw bottles to the musicians, destroyed everything they got to hold of. I have seen J—— throw chairs to the Coleman, Optimus lamps, bottles of whiskey. While I was still outside, some of them began throwing again at me broken bottles. I was hit in the leg. When everything inside the Blue Goose Club was quiet, they went home toward the wharf. All of them about fifteen sailors."

FROM: EXEC
TO: C.O.

The following men returned at 2300 after being involved in a fight at the Blue Goose:

P——, S 1/c Nearly unconscious. Either drunk or badly beaten up.

T——, S 2/c Drunk but unhurt.

O——, F 2/c Very bad cut on head and bruises on face.

S——, S 2/c Cuts on face and bruised hands.

L——, S 1/c Very drunk but unhurt.

T——, S 1/c Sober and only witnessed fight.

P——, S 1/c Drunk but unhurt.

S——, MM 1/c Drunk and cut and bruised about the face and hands.

T——, PhM 2/c Was ashore but returned sober and treated injuries.

K——, S 1/c Was duty S.P. He witnessed fight but was sober and unhurt.

THE BILL OF JOSÉ SORREÁL:

1 Coleman lamp	P 60.00
1 Optimus lamp	180.00

2 iron chair at P 6.00	12.00
1 improvised chair wooden	5.00
3 improvised wooden chair	30.00
1 glass jar	15.00
2 Bot. Whiskey (3) Feathers (Big)	40.00
Total	P 342.00

The above itemized articles with their prices are true and correct. Therefore I affixed my signature below at Mariveles, Bataan.

(Sgd)   José Sorreál
Owner of Blue Goose Bar.

A Sailor's Verse:

Have you ever been in the Philippines—
The place is full of pom-pom queens,
The clap is high and the syphilis worse,
So beat your meat for safety first.
> Drinking Rum and Coca-Cola
> Go down point to Manila
> Both mother and daughter
> Working for the sailor's dollar.

The women with their dirty feet
Roam up and down the village street,
One comes up and whispers low,
"You want to buy some pom-pom, Joe?"
> Chorus

The pom-pom house is a bamboo shack,
There all the girls a-lay on their back,
The rates for it are very high,
So use a rubber to keep it dry.
> Chorus

The pom-pom girls are very smart,
They make you pay before you start,
The pom-pom here is very nice,
But ten pesos is a hell of a price!
> Chorus

Statement of R——, S 2/c, USNR: "We left here about eight minutes to eleven last night and started over and we got about halfway between this BCL and this tug. This rowboat was coming out and we couldn't see him anywhere. We hit him, and bumped along the side and K—— asked me what it was and I told him I thought it was a board. We turned the spotlight around and saw there was a boat we'd hit. One fellow was right there at the boat, and the other one was about ten foot from him. This fellow on the boat was hollering that the other one couldn't swim. K—— dived in about even with the boat and went swimming after the fellow. He got him back to the VP and I got ahold of him, but someway he slipped out of my hand. He went under."

I took this down directly on the typewriter, easily, for the boy stopped frequently to swallow hard. He asked if he could smoke a cigarette. I wanted to accuse him and say, "But if you had held onto the man, he wouldn't have drowned!" However, the boy knew this.

The evidence of the coxswain confirmed that of the boat hook. I worked the two into a formal report, and the yeoman made up a copy to send ashore to the Army.

It was a Sunday morning; a church party of one had gone ashore. We had been in Mariveles four months, and it was beginning to pale because the charm, the bloom, had worn off. It was no longer simply quaint and amusing. We hung on, loathsomely.

Our main trouble involved a theft of four thousand pounds of sugar from our own dry dock by our own men. We never did find out who did it. They sold the sugar on the black market at something like a dollar a pound; but the Filipinos tricked them, paying them in prewar Philippine National Bank notes, which were now worthless. The big fight at the Blue Goose had that undercurrent of crime to it.

The Army men in the rowboat were from another base and were not connected in any way to our sugar theft; but they were rowing in the darkness because their boat motor had been stolen while they were ashore.

Everything seemed a rottenness, like our man sent to jail because he had beaten up his mistress—pistol-whipped her in the presence of witnesses. It all made me sick at heart— the war, the peace, equally.

That Sunday evening, I had an unexpected visitor, a chaplain. He wanted as much detail as he could concerning the drowned man, because, you see, he had to write a letter of condolence to his wife. Would I help? It wasn't as if the man had been killed in action, and so what could he say? Nor had he ever met the deceased; and besides, he was just out from the States and had never done this sort of thing. What should we say?

Together, we worked up something, referring to my dictionary of synonyms, trying to write a letter that was not trite, that did not quite give all the facts, yet was not untruthful.

In the outcome, the chaplain coveted my dictionary. Would I trade it, he wanted to know? And the next day he brought in trade for my dictionary five bottles of Communion wine.

CORREGIDOR

~~~~~~~~~~~~~~~~~

ON DECEMBER 8, 1941, Japanese planes bombed, in a somewhat leisurely way, American air fields near Manila, weeding out any possible defense of the area. On December 10, the Cavite Navy Yard southwest of Manila was destroyed; simultaneously, Japanese invasion troops were landed in the north of Luzon. The Army of the Philippines delayed that onslaught as long as possible, but there were no reinforcements and no new supplies, and only the hope of them to keep the men going. On March 12, General MacArthur was ordered out. On April 9, 1942, some sixty or seventy thousand starving Americans and Filipinos surrendered near Mariveles. There were left in the area only the forces on Corregidor, an island fortress a mile long, at the entrance to Manila Bay. This was subjected to heavy bombardment by the Japanese. Finally, on May 6, 1942, Corregidor surrendered too.

Some five thousand Japanese troops were stationed on Corregidor, and they were there in January 1945 when American planes began their bombing raids. Some thirty-

two hundred *tons* of explosives were dropped on the island
before our invasion. On February 16 (Mariveles had been
secured on February 15), amphibious craft landed on the
north side of the island while paratroops were dropped on
top, in the area of the former parade ground and on a small
golf course. The Japanese retreated to caves, but all re-
sistance ended by February 26. The cost: two hundred and
twenty-five American dead, four thousand five hundred
Japanese known dead plus an estimated five hundred
Japanese buried alive in the caves. General MacArthur returned on March 2 for the flag-raising on the Rock.

"I see that the old flagpole still stands," MacArthur said
to the Colonel Jones, whose men had retaken the island.
"Have your troops hoist the colors to its peak, and let no
enemy ever haul them down."

There was something horrifying about the American reliance on an island fortress. The big guns topside and the
Malinta Tunnel to the east, protection against bombing for
thousands, were considered invulnerable and hence the base
for a prewar military society of what seems now to be an incredible naïveté: the parade ground, the golf course, the
Marine band, the prominent military barracks topsides, the
little streetcar track down to the tunnel, the fantastic scenery of bay and mountains and tropical sunsets, to say nothing of Filipino houseboys and Chinese amahs. General Mac-
Arthur spoke of the "languorous laze" of the Philippines,
but all that vanished in the war. The barracks on top were
guidelines for the Japanese bombers; the large guns were
soon destroyed; the command had to move to the tunnel.
During bombardments, the ventilation in the tunnel had to
be shut off; the latrines had always been inadequate; no one
had conceived of around-the-clock bombing; and of course
the main tunnel and the side tunnels weren't big enough to
hold everybody on the island (and there are hints in mem-
oirs of a vicious "in" society and an "out" society). Everyone
held on as long as possible and was brave, but what was the

sense in such a helpless defensive posture? Finally, one either came out of the caves with his hands up or was entombed there permanently. (The NORAD command post under Cheyenne Mountain in Colorado is a part of such archaic thinking.)

By October 1945, Corregidor was a tourist stop. Here was the Malinta Tunnel, the entrance nearly blocked by rubble, and, just inside, in the dark, an unbelievable stench. Here were the trolley tracks draped in great curves over dead trees. Here were the barracks, three stories of gutted concrete abstractions, the stairs leading nowhere. Here was the flag of MacArthur, and over here, Japanese prisoners of war put to work with wheelbarrows to dump rubble into the innumerable shell craters.

I must add that walking by myself on a grassy path I stumbled across a human skull. Nearby were a Japanese helmet, the two halves of a pelvic bone, a thigh bone, and some dried pieces of boots. I cannot recall the procession of thought through my mind at the time—I was not unmindful of the souvenir skull of Saipan—but I mark a change. With a stick, I *arranged* these objects and photographed them. I believe now that this was wrong. My purpose, I suppose, was to take a picture that would epitomize the war, and I lavished care on the subsequent enlargement, and I have it still in my album of photographs. But what I see when I look at the picture is that a reasonably mature and intelligent man had, in a sense, violated a human grave. The picture epitomized me, and it shames me.

MANILA

〜〜〜〜〜〜

ON CHRISTMAS EVE, 1941, the Army evacuated Manila, MacArthur declaring it an open city "without the characteristics of a military objective." Our Army withdrew to the north, moving counterclockwise around the bay to defensive positions on Bataan. Manila remained in Japanese hands from then until 1945. American troops began their invasion of the island of Luzon in January 1945 and swiftly encircled Manila, which troops entered on February 3.[1] The Japanese, like the Americans, had not planned to defend Manila, but when their withdrawal routes were cut off, they chose to fight "to the bitter end," all twenty

1 On that date, prisoners of war at Santo Tomas and Bildad prisons were freed on the urgent order of MacArthur to take those objectives first. Most American servicemen in the Pacific in World War II were bitterly anti-MacArthur. He seemed too grand, too self-centered and publicity-seeking. I shared this feeling for twenty years, until I discovered that a neighbor of mine, who had been in bad health since the war, had been a prisoner of war in Manila. MacArthur had come on a tour of inspection to the room where my neighbor and another man lay on the floor, too emaciated and sick to rise when he entered. General MacArthur took off his raincoat, knelt, and placed it around the shoulders of my neighbor—and the man has kept the raincoat these twenty years.

thousand of them. In the month of February, in the course of weeding out the Japs, the city was destroyed by our artillery fire and by Japanese demolition. The naval historian Morison described it as a more complete destruction than that of Cologne, Hamburg, or London. It was an unforgettable sight.

The Army at Mariveles gave us a tug to use for our weekly trips to Manila for supplies. These were not simple trips. Our food we had to get from the *Gold Star,* a supply ship in the harbor. Our mail came from the Fleet Post Office on the Pasig River (my wooden box, mailed from Ulithi six months earlier, finally came to the Harrison Street transshipment warehouse). Miscellaneous items (such as the freon-gas bombs with which to kill cockroaches) we could get from a repair ship. Our payroll came from the Navy's Wilson Building in downtown Manila (and if you want to feel really uneasy, try carrying around $4,000 in cash in Manila). Our paperwork had to be done some five miles south of the city at the Pacific Sea Frontier command. We would also stop at the Red Cross building for free lemonade or at the Army PX to buy beer. We spent one day trying to locate our enlisted man whose jaw had been broken in the Blue Goose fight, but there were too many Army hospitals in the area, and we never did find him.

Just to get to Manila took four hours. Sometimes we would leave Mariveles at 0600 and return after dark that same night; other times, we spent the night at a dock near PacSeaFron headquarters, sleeping on the deck of the tug. But we did not mind that part of the trip. To ride in to Manila was to be Captain of one's own ship, even if it was only a forty-foot wooden tug. The boat crew needed no directives. All one had to do was sit in a deck chair under the awning aft or in the sunlight, drink vile coffee and talk, or watch the scenery (native fishermen or an aircraft carrier that loomed above us the size of Corregidor), or simply read. The bay was usually as smooth as glass.

Once, we circled around to the south side of Corregidor
and stopped at an anchored boat where divers were at work
bringing up two million silver pesos that had been cached
there in 1942. One of our men had been loaned out as a
diver, and so we all got souvenirs.

Approaching Manila, the first time, there didn't seem to
be anything wrong. There were ships in the harbor and tall
buildings beyond. Gradually, as the tug moved closer, we
discovered that a dozen of the ships were Japanese, and they
were sunk in the shallow water, only their superstructures
and tall smokestacks showing. The buildings of downtown
Manila—slowly we realized that they were walls surrounding nothing.

We steered for the boat landing on the Pasig River, riding
under the temporary Bailey bridges. Down the muddy
water drifted great masses of water hyacinths with their
lavender blooms. And there drifted too an odor I cannot
describe or forget—of mud and dust simultaneously, of
decay, burning, rot, garbage, filth, excrement, and the sweetness of the tropics—and beside us now these great shells of
buildings.

We landed and went to see the sights. We walked, we
hitch-hiked, we rode in jeeps converted into buses (jeep-
neys), and in the tiny two-wheeled pony carts (*calesas*). We
visited the Chinese markets and, in the course of the winter,
half a hundred bars. I never knew any Filipinos in Manila
and so never saw beyond the façades, but it was enough—
quite enough to transform one's entire life.

I remember a downtown street and one particular building. It was a five-story apartment building of reinforced
concrete. A demolition bomb had neatly knocked down the
supporting columns on the left, and the whole building had
slipped sideways, staying partly upright at about a sixty-
degree angle. Some of the front slabs had fallen off into a
great pile to the left; some of the slabs dangled in the air,
held by the reinforcing rods. Three unshattered windows

hung *beneath* their frames. The pile of rubble to the side contained concrete staircases that had slid down and out. The building showed some damage from gunfire, but it had obviously been purposely demolished by the Japanese on their way out of the city. It did not represent the death of any people (who cares, after twenty years, about the deaths of the thousands and thousands in this one city?), but to me, it was tragedy, futility, emptiness.

The rubble of the building had been pushed back out of the street, and shops set up. That is, in front of the wall of trash were wooden counters and poles that supported tin roofs to provide shade. The clerks stood in front of these counters and they were in business: sandals, jade, bananas, Java sparrows in wicker cages, peanuts, raisins, ivory elephants, mandarin jackets, ornate daggers, decorated buffalo horns, amber, liquor, books, papayas, ice cream, silk scarves —the economy boomed.

I could not accept this. Whose fault was it? What are buildings for if they must be destroyed? I had been an architectural student before the war. Manila was a nightmare. What was I to do?

On Monday, February 11, 1946, I rode in a jeep with a Filipino driver and three of our enlisted men, taking mail sacks back to our tug, the men already in their whites, impatient for an afternoon of liberty. South on Dewey Boulevard, at the entrance to a large residence, we noticed a cardboard sign on the dividing strip, "War Crime Trials," and stopped to question the MP at the gate.

"Yessir, the trials are open to anyone in proper uniform. Your men are okay, but, sir, you'd have to have on your jacket. You oughtta come. They're gonna give the death verdict today to that general, the Beast of Bataan, what's-his-name."

I left the three men to hold a place in line while I went to the tug with the mail, made the driver wait while I changed, and then went back. Homma. General Homma.

Recall that in April 1942, the Army of the Philippines had surrendered to the Japanese in the Mariveles area on the southern tip of Bataan. General Masaharu Homma was the man in charge of the whole Japanese operation, and he had been under terrific pressure from Tokyo to speed up the conquest of the Philippines. His primary problem was to bring his own troops south for the final assault on Corregidor; the prisoners of war were a secondary problem and an obstacle. They would have to be moved out of the battle area. They would have to walk north nineteen miles to Balanga, where some two hundred trucks would take them thirty-six miles to San Fernando, where they would then be transferred to freight cars for the ride north to Capas, and then marched a final eight miles to a concentration camp, Camp O'Donnell. General Homma turned over the details of this maneuver to his transportation officer, Colonel Tushimitsu Takatsu, who carried out the plan. Field hospitals were set up, "resting areas" were designated, rations were brought south to Balanga, supposedly the end of the first day's march from Mariveles—all told, a simple enough tactical problem. But the Japanese had presumed that there were only some thirty thousand prisoners; further, that they would have their own rations for the first day's march; and further, that they were in reasonable health. But in fact there were over seventy thousand starving men without food or water, prostrated by malaria or the extreme heat or their own despair. Chaos resulted.

From the military point of view, the march was disorganized, uncoordinated, and inadequately supervised. Some prisoners were given transportation and rode all the way to Camp O'Donnell. Others walked, with adequate food and rest. Some thousands of captured Filipinos simply escaped into the jungle or the sugarcane fields. Many died along the road from malaria, exhaustion, or starvation, and would have died had they stayed where they were. But *thousands* died on the march, and no one knows how many from the brutality of the guards—except that there were countless atrocities.

When the news of the Death March leaked out, the American people were horrified, and after the war ended they sought, shall I say, redress. MacArthur denied that "revenge and passion" had anything to do with military justice. It was to him a case of military transgression, a violation of a "fundamental code of chivalry." There had been "savageries," "infamy," "depravity" in the Japanese guards, and "Soldiers of an army invariably reflect the attitude of their general. The leader is the essence." Therefore, General Homma was responsible "before the bar of universal justice." I measure his words (reviewing the court's verdict) against the laconic attitude of the MP who told us on February 11 *before* the court's verdict, "They're gonna give the death verdict today to the Beast of Bataan."

When I got back, there were two long lines of men (mostly enlisted men) on the grass in front of the two-story building (rich green, mowed grass; but the building was pock-marked with bullet holes). We watched several Army limousines draw up at the entrance and discharge gold-braid officers whom we could not identify. After a few minutes the lines starting moving inside, past an old Filipino policewoman, then right and left around a rather shabby patio lined with a dozen MP's.

"Roll your sleeves down, bud. Cut out the talking. Put out that cigarette. Hats off, now."

The court room was formerly a ballroom, with a slick terrazzo floor, green walls, an arched ceiling, and gray marble pilasters spacing three small balconies on each side. We were crowded into chairs at the rear of the ballroom, facing west. The court would sit at a broad table in front of an arc of floor-length windows, through which one could see the sparkle of sunlight on the water of the bay, the half-sunken Japanese ships, the dim shape of Corregidor and Bataan in the distance. Over the table was a string of spotlights. Movie cameras were on platforms to each side, and several photographers moved around focusing their cameras. We waited. The MP's ushered more gold braid, Army and Navy, down to the front seats, some of them escorting WAC's or pretty girls in Red Cross uniforms. There were only a few Filipinos in the room.

After some thirty minutes, an MP officer in charge stepped to a microphone and asked for our attention. He reviewed the formalities of court procedure, sternly warned us not to smoke, and said, concerning General Homma, "In a decision like this there is, of course, nervous tension. You must prepare yourself mentally for a decision favorable or unfavorable to the defendant so that when the verdict is read there will be no audible whisper or unnecessary noise." He repeated the statement slowly, as if speaking to children, and added, "If the commission is adjourned instead of recessed after the verdict is read, come to attention while the commission leaves the courtroom. Do not leave until ordered to; do not talk. The verdict is not to be discussed until you have left the building and the grounds."

It took just that to create tension and an audible buzz. No one seemed to notice General Homma enter the room until flash bulbs went off and the movie cameras started to whir. We all strained and stretched to have a look at him before he sat down. He was a small man, dressed in a gray suit, white shirt, green necktie. His head was bald, shiny, red. He did not look particularly Oriental. His brow was furrowed with worry or concern. His bearing was elegant, though his shoulders drooped in a certain humbleness. In the States he could have passed freely as a small businessman, a grocer, or a bank clerk.

When the prisoner was seated, several clerks filed in: Army officers and enlisted men, two or three WAC's, one of whom looked like a movie star. It was now three o'clock, a minute or two after. The spotlights had been turned on, the warm room became hot.

Someone boomed, "Attention!" and everyone stood. The

commission walked in, their faces rigid, their dignity some-what marred by their khaki shirts and open collars. They sat, and we were told to sit. A speaker for the commission remained standing and ordered the accused to stand, with an interpreter to his right, one of the defense lawyers on his left.

Then the charges were read: "Masaharu Homma, com-manding general of the Philippines between 8 December, 1941, and 15 August, 1944 [the dates were changed in the verdict to December 10 and August 5], did unlawfully . . . brutal atrocities and other high crimes . . . on 6 May, 1942, refused water to prisoners of war. . . . Does the accused desire to make a statement?"

The interpreter whispered to General Homma, and then the general spoke himself, in good English, in a voice not humble, not as if he meant what he said, but as if he too were carrying out a formality: "I wish to thank the gentle-men of the commission for the courteous ways I have been treated through the entire trial. I thank you very much." He bowed slightly, then straightened.

"Findings of the commission . . . secret written ballot re-quiring a two-thirds or more vote . . . guilty . . . except for the dates . . . and not guilty of the charge of refusing water . . ."

There was a slight, a terrible pause before the man continued.

"By secret written ballot . . . the commission sentences the accused Masaharu Homma to be shot to death by musketry.

"The commission is adjourned *sine die*."

That night we stayed over in the boat harbor of PacSeaFron because three of us had bought for twelve dol-lars a bottle of sparkling burgundy. We didn't have enough ice to get it very cold, and it didn't sparkle very much, but it added something to our fried steaks and fried potatoes. We felt on a par with the admiral whose yacht was tied up at the next dock. Music and the laughter of women drifted across the dark water to our tug. We loafed on the lumpy canvas bags of mail and drank our sparkling burgundy out of tin cups, not envious of the admiral.

We talked, of course, about Homma. I wish I could remember in more detail what we said; I had taken notes at the court session and do not have to rely on my memory for that; but of the night, I can't even remember which men were in on the talk. We commented, I know, on what a circus it had been and then we seemed to hear, time and again, the volley of "muskets" that would, later on, end the life of General Homma. We agreed that the knowledge of the certainty of death was a pitiable thing and yet we were so outraged by what Homma had done or what he stood for that we thought shooting too good for him. Of course we were noncombatants who had not seen death close by,

but we sympathized with the rationale of the law. However, I no longer do.

I suppose everyone in Manila at that time heard the ghostly echo of rifle shots. I wish I could go back, these twenty years later, to investigate—but I suppose I know without actually going that the sounds of snipers, demolition squads, and executioners have vanished completely. Still, I would expect to be able somewhere in the city to find that dreadful odor of the past.

I resumed my reading:

Soc.   Then we must do no wrong?

Cr.   Certainly not.

Soc.   Nor when injured injure in return, as the many imagine; for we must injure no one at all?

Cr.   Clearly not.

Soc.   Again, Crito, may we do evil?

Cr.   Surely not, Socrates.

Soc.   And what of doing evil in return for evil, which is the morality of the many—is that just or not?

Cr.   Not just.

Soc.   For doing evil to another is the same as injuring him?

Cr.   Very true.

Soc.   Then we ought not to retaliate or render evil for evil to any one, whatever evil we may have suffered from him. But I would have you consider, Crito, whether you really mean what you are saying. For this opinion has never been held, and never will be held, by any considerable number of persons; and those who are agreed and those who are not agreed upon this point have no common ground, and can only despise one another when they see how widely they differ. Tell me, then, whether you agree with and assent to my first principle, that neither injury nor retaliation or warding off evil by evil is ever right.

JAPAN

~~~~~~~~~~~~~~~~~~~~~~~~

NOVEMBER 7, 1945. Dear Web: Shep is here
and he's going to take me to Japan!—if the Skipper says I
can go—and I won't mail this until we do go, but right now,
it's not certain. Skipper may object to putting his name on
leave papers that are strictly illegal, although Shep says we
won't be anywhere near a Shore Patrol. Airily, he says that
(drunkenly, too, in his stately way). He says, I will take you
to Ultima Thule, says it as if it were in the next room. We'll
forge you some leave papers; in case you get into trouble,
you can wave them around importantly.

But I'd better start eight hours ago, when he arrived.
It's 0200 now. I can't sleep, of course, so I'll write. Thank
God I wrote and told him where this hellhole is. In case
you're around, drop in, I wrote, thinking at the time that
he wouldn't, but he did. Remember when he left? It's been
almost three years. Who can believe what has happened to
all of us in these three bloody years? (In the first place, we
survived.) However, remember Shep when he left—he was
so unperturbed, so cool, so arrogant; and we thought it was

all a show to cover up his immaturity. Well, he doesn't
seem to have changed at all. He doesn't show any emotion;
he's as calm and slow-moving as ever. I suppose it's just what
an Air Force officer ought to be, and all I can say is, if it is a
show, it's a damn good show.

You can imagine how *I* felt when he discovered me on
this garbage can—as if he had lived these three years in the
splendor of the sky. He sniffed, oh God, ever so delicately,
but he *sniffed,* although he had the good manners *not* to
say, "Of course, Lee, it's the sort of place one would have
expected you to end up in." Well, as it turned out, he
envied me! Or rather he envied the food, my having my
own room, and the shower. He let that slip, that he hadn't
had a decent shower bath for the eighteen months he's been
overseas—it's hard to believe. (In the second place, though
we survived, we are probably *not unscathed*—does this
make sense? Maybe I can explain it later.)

Anyway, to cut this short, Shep landed at Clark Field
yesterday in a C-47. He's a navigator only. They're ferrying
planes down here from some air field near Tokyo, planes
that will be left out in the field, abandoned. His crew will
hitch a ride back Monday or Tuesday, and I can go along
if that bastard of a captain isn't a bastard. It took Shep all
day to get here: a jeep to Manila, lucky enough to find out
about the Army's boat to Mariveles, and then doubly lucky
to find the dock it left from *and* get there just before it
pulled out. As it happened, I was at the gangplank when he
came up, watched him, wondered who it was, finally recognized him, wanted to shout at him. Instead, he saluted
properly and requested permission to come on board. Manners, always. But he was *wrinkled*—his clothes, I mean. Not
quite what you would expect.

Well, I did my best to unwrinkle the rest of him. I
introduced him to Skipper, *told* Skipper I was taking the
evening off, talked to the mess boy about later, then took
Shep ashore to the Blue Goose. We were there maybe three

hours, talking mostly. (Remember how no matter how much Shep used to drink, he never showed it? Well, he does now, a little.) It was very pleasant. We reestablished that relationship the three of us used to have—never very close, I'll admit, but close enough so that you knew that the person you were talking to cared about what it was you said. Shep has been everywhere out here. He's been shot at, nearly bombed (he uses his hands to tell about all this, just like they do in the movies). He's even shot at Japs himself (with a machine gun, so far above them, on a jungle trail, there wasn't any risk of hitting anybody)—and in a sense all he really wants to talk about is death. (Imagine what it would be like if nobody else cared about what you did.) Anyway, we got high enough to talk that way, and about midnight we got a boat back. The mess boy had everything set out for us and cooked us a steak with garlic; it was tough, sure, but it was rare and it was good. And then he said simply, "Why don't you take off and fly back to Tokyo with me?" Well, you know, it is one thing to hear about somebody else doing things like that, but to be involved *yourself*—

It is late, and I've got to get some sleep. There's a bed of sorts made up for me here in the wardroom. Shep has my room. He was in the shower half an hour. We typed up leave papers for the Skipper to sign. I'm sober now. I want to say, tritely, what does the future hold? I mean, simply, what's going to happen to us tomorrow? What will become of us? And does it matter? There was this undercurrent, you see, to the talk tonight, the fact that we had come through three years of war, and wondering why, was it just chance? Luck? And what happens next? And nothing Shep said would make it real to me—what it is like to be in Tokyo *now,* so soon after the war. Neither of us (or you either, for that matter) is what a person would think of as a *conqueror* (you know what I mean, Romans, all that, the Rape of the Sabine Women). Who is the conqueror, who is victorious, if it is not us?

I'll get some more coffee and then try to sleep. If we go,
I can mail this in Manila tomorrow. Today, I mean. And
then Japan! Me! How the hell can I get to sleep?

November 9. Two days later! If we haven't left yet,
at least we're headed in the right direction! We're at Clark
Field, north of Manila, waiting for I don't know what red
tape. They've all gone off in a truck somewhere for a meeting and left the rest of us sitting in the plane. The "us" is
about twenty-four people trying to bum a ride to Tokyo,
like the two Red Cross girls with more gear than they can
handle *plus* a puppy, a terrier of some sort; they've given
up for today and gone back to a barracks on the other side
of the field. Like the Army chaplain who must weigh two
hundred pounds and has some eleven pieces of luggage *plus*
an *organ* in a canvas case. He thinks we're going to fly *that*
to Tokyo, too. "They" are the crews of the five planes that
flew down here together, four planes to be left, and the fifth
to carry everybody back.

(A plane taxis by, and I stop long enough to watch it
take off. Of course I can't identify it, but imagine the plane
for yourself, the bright-green sugar-cane fields, the Bataan
mountains to the southwest, the valley all morning haze—
absolutely pleasant and peaceful.)

They are great guys. The ones we had dinner with and
whose names I remember are as follows. Lieutenant Kinsreth from a small town near Des Moines—a typically
healthy, clean, religious type. Lieutenant Ruml, also from
Iowa, die-hard Republican, pug nose, lively, good guy.
Lieutenant Hamlin from Tennessee, good-looking, very
easy, big cheekbones, casual. Lieutenant Somebody—I guess
I've forgotten his name already—but the point is that they
are all pleasant, all very young (about twenty-four, twenty-
five); nobody swears very much or drinks very much; nobody tells dirty jokes; everybody is well-mannered, polite—

it's like a club, and so damn different from some of the slobs I've had to live with the last three years. They are *innocent,* for God's sake! Pilots? Warriors? Conquerors? They talk like their mothers were listening. It's like a parlor game, and the chilling thought is that I've got to trust my life to these *children* who think they can get this enormous plane out of this pasture today or tomorrow, up into the goddam impalpable air! They aren't old enough! They seem fit for fraternity tea dances—nothing more. How could we win the war with these *boys?*

You should have seen me sleeping on a cot last night, outside. A couple of planes came in during the night—and noisy! My God, I shot right up in the air! And you should have seen me trying to shave this morning out of somebody's helmet liner and with cold water yet. It's a good thing I didn't bring my dress blues. What a primitive life! Poor Shep, who likes the amenities so much—to have to live like this. I know he will grow up to be rich and conservative in his old age.

Anyway, last night, the five of us hitch-hiked to San Fernando. We drank (a little) and had dinner in a Chinese restaurant (four tables, in a corner building, big glass windows, watching everybody go by). We had fried chicken (expensive—two dollars), and you have never seen such pitiful, small, meatless birds. After we finished, everybody ordered the same thing all over again. Afterward, we went with everybody else to the square to watch a little outdoor stage show. The crowd of people was like a Saturday night at home, only these were all *short* people. But the stage show was like nothing I had ever seen. Oh sure, colored lights, a magician, a knife thrower, hula dancers, a comedian—it looked like the members of one family, and everybody had a specialty. Then they put on a play, a bedroom farce—you know, husband, wife, lover, maid, people hiding behind screens, the husband unwittingly setting up the affair between his wife and her lover—and all this in Tagalog, and you didn't need the words to understand the action; but the audience roared at the jokes, at the husband particularly, done up in a white face, like a clown. So somebody translated for us and explained. It seems this was a farce imported from Spain in the nineteenth century, and it had been popular in the provinces ever since. Well, you know, I had to pinch myself to be sure I was real. To top it off, the guy who translated for us was a Filipino sergeant—he showed us his ID card to boast of his rank—a little tough guy, but more! He had been on the Death March of Bataan! How was it? we asked. "Eet wass bad," he said, "very bad." That! And the farce going on—and to be there in the midst of it!

When it was over, we all went back to the plane and sat under the wing of the plane and talked. Somebody started to sing songs, and everybody joined in—you know, just ordinary songs, but the black shape of the wing blotting the stars, and the mild breeze with the strange smell of sugar cane—and the dots of lights on the runway, and the airplane beacon lighting us at intervals—*Where are we?* I wanted to say, *Why are we here?*

November 10, Okinawa. They have all gone to a movie, which I pretended I had seen, so I would have time to write. They should have gone to a church and spent the night praying that they could get out of here safe and sound! I am more than half serious, nearly frantic in fact, and would take a boat back to Mariveles if I could. My God, they are children playing with toys which will kill us all!

"Well, if the weather up ahead doesn't get any worse, I think we ought to give it a try. Anything is better than staying around here." So said Lieutenant Kinsreth. Imagine!

I asked Shep, "Are they *kidding?*"

He shrugged no. "It's all chance."

"No skill? No common sense?"

He said no, very little. "Chance."

He was upset, I know, being a little tight-lipped and melodramatic about lighting a cigarette in the middle of a sentence. So determined not to show any emotion—they have, damn it, seen too many movies.

The point is that a plane crashed right here, two hours before we landed. Shep and his friends knew all the men, five of them, who were killed. They were from the same air base in Japan and down here between orders. They'd gone up—it occurs to me how much of this may be sheer rumor, for the stories were all word-of-mouth, passed around in an office—still, there is the *fact* of their deaths. The pilot had called the flight so they could pile up air hours toward discharge. The pilot and the navigator had to hunt up the radio operator, who was playing bridge. Told that he didn't have to go up, he said first that he wouldn't; then that he would; finally, that he wouldn't; and so he is alive. The navigator actually said to him, "We who are about to die salute you," and went off and died. Rumor has it that the pilot buzzed a friend on a ship in the harbor, dove down too low, and couldn't pull out.

Not chance, but *games*.

Yet it had been such a beautiful day. We left Clark Field about 0800, and the flight here, one thousand miles, took seven hours. You should have seen us all—bucket seats, Army, Navy, Marines, the women, their dog, the chaplain, his organ, dozens of suitcases, duffle bags, mail bags, packages—it wasn't a plane, it was a freight car, or it was like trying to get a whale airborne. The C-47 roared down the runway for ten or fifteen minutes, it seemed, before it could get up enough speed to get off the ground. Shep was not navigating; he sat beside me and said at intervals, "Christ!" and again, "Christ!" and when we were up, he turned on me for being so ignorant that I wasn't frightened and then lectured me for an hour on the danger of take-offs and landings.

I didn't care! Not *then*. Shep had a navigation map, and

we located on the map what we could see outside, and it was such a slow and leisurely flight, up along, beside, the chain of mountains, and then the sea, so sudden, with such a bright turquoise in the water at the land's edge, and then the deep purple of the sea, the patterns of waves, tiny boats, and we actually flew over an island with a smoking volcano, then chains of islands, and the sea again—and people crowding over you to work their way to the john, some enlisted men sprawled asleep in the passageway, and the dog getting sick, the smell all in the cabin, and when we managed to get as high as nine thousand feet, it got so billy-o cold in the cabin I could have—

I didn't want it to end, ever, but we came down finally. There was Okinawa, ships in the harbor, red dirt on the hills, and the most curious horseshoe shapes out in the fields —and then the minute we landed, the news about the crash.

Shep and I went walking. The horseshoes turned out to be tombs. The *omega* shape was a stone wall with a grassy hollow in the middle and several tombs beneath the stone wall. So we found one of these and sat on the wall and smoked cigarettes and talked about death, chance.

So then after chow (Spam), they checked the weather map to Japan, and all I know is that it looked bad and they said they'd go ahead in the morning; and then they all went off to the movies.

I don't know—as I've said, the day has put me on edge. If I had any guts I'd make a fuss and refuse to fly with them tomorrow, and take a boat back, but how could I explain to the Navy what I was doing here in the first place? It isn't like the war, when you had no choice at all—or is it that much different? I'd feel safer if just one of Shep's friends smoked a cigar or told a dirty joke or showed some outward sign of being mature in his judgment. They are so young. Instead, they'll fly into bad weather tomorrow simply to avoid being bored by staying here in Okinawa. They don't go to funerals, they go to the movies!

•   •   •

November 11, Tachikawa. (Imagine, actually being here.) I've learned this much, at any rate, even if I never get back, that the presence of death is inalterably tied to beauty, is a requisite for it; that it is death which is the intoxication, the intensifier; by extension, it explains the war. This may sound like a Solemn Pronouncement. I guess it is. I've got my reasons.

We spent a wretched night at the transit camp at Okinawa. We slept in tents, and the night was very cold (but not half as cold as it is here). Shep got a spider bite on his lower lip, which swelled so he could hardly talk. We made it to the plane before 0800, certain, however, that the plane wouldn't leave with the bad weather ahead, but Lieutenant Kinsreth and his crew drove up in a jeep, cheery as all hell, and said they were going to give it a try.

In less than an hour, these wisps of cloud began to float by; then, within minutes, cloud obscured everything. Kinsreth climbed back up into sunlight above the solid blanket of clouds. Periodically, we ran into the peaks of clouds; and the daylight dimmed; then we'd hear the engine sound change, and up we went into the sunlight again. Below us were peaks and valleys of clouds, the map having, as it were, boiled up towards us. Then Kinsreth shifted course slightly; we could look ahead and see what the trouble was—the clouds were a solid purple-colored barrier between us and Japan. We'd have to go higher still.

Pretty soon, everyone began putting on their coats and jackets, sharing the few blankets there were. Shep huddled up to me and swore, muttering through his swollen lip that Kinsreth should have turned back, the frigging plane was overweight, the engines needed servicing, and if Kinsreth wasn't so pigheaded, but no, he was up there in the cockpit with an oxygen mask on, and he didn't give a damn if the passangers froze to death or passed out. We were at 13,000 feet. Even so, going over the cloud bank would be easier than going through or under. There was an elation in the lack of oxygen and the cold. One would soon drift off to sleep forever. And ahead, the clouds were purple-black and still higher than the plane.

So the plane banked and circled slowly for half an hour— while the pilot, copilot, and navigator debated what to do. Shep and I tried to keep a sense of direction from the angle of the sun, but, looking out, it was evident that the clouds had boiled up on all sides of the plane, that there was no simple retreat possible any more. The decision was to go *under* the clouds, and so down we went, for hours, the plane buffeted by the mountains of clouds—dark, light, shafts of sunlight—and loose bags tumbling about in the passageway —then everything gray for long minutes until we did come out *under* the clouds, the ocean black beneath us, whitecaps all too visible, and we stabilized and flew at an altitude of only one thousand feet.

Shep swore again. Great, he said, and what do we do when we reach the mainland—three-thousand-foot mountains right down to the water's edge.

So there we flew, more ship than plane, for another hour. And then, then the clouds sloped down onto the water and we flew *gray,* even the windows, the portholes, obscured by beads of water from what must have been pouring rain outside.

I liked that, very much. I liked the reaching out and the great calm after surrendering life itself to mere chance.

The navigator, at a tiny desk in the passageway to the cockpit, kept getting up and looking out the window, hoping to see water, to estimate from the whitecaps the side thrust of the waves and hence how far off course the plane had drifted with the winds. He guessed. He had to guess— and he suddenly rushed up to the cockpit to confer with the pilot. The plane tilted to the right. We stared out the port window, and, seconds later, there it was, on the left, unreal, a black mountain, ringed with white breakers above the shallow, emerald-green water. We were *that close.* And so, *because we had been in danger,* we were able to see through the drifting clouds ahead a rhythmic series of mountains, the color of water, suspended above the water, the mist, exactly as in a Japanese painting, a kind of timeless delight.

I have trouble even now, the next day, actually *here,* trying to feel *actually here.* Some kind of acute transformation took place in that flight, in the glimpse of absolutes, I suppose, as if the plane were changed into a bird, a fish—no, I give up. The rest of the flight was absolutely stunning. The mountains became solid; there were trees on them, dull brown and gold. There were bright-green rice fields and black wet highways, and a bicycle, a yellow parasol, and we were on the ground, the aisle of the plane suddenly sloping uphill.

Perhaps I should skip over the rest; but everybody has gone to another meeting this morning, and there's nothing for me to do but wait for Shep to come back and try to keep warm. I haven't seen anything in Japan yet except the air base! I'll keep writing till they come, and anyway, you see, the point of the whole *flight* is in the fact that I came at last, after three years, to the enemy, a specific man, the man responsible for this whole crazy war.

Well, we landed, and much as I wanted to get out and look around, Shep said we should stay right in the plane and try to keep warm until transportation arrived. And when the cargo doors were opened, you can't imagine the *wet cold blast* of air that came in. Desolate! The whole air field. Dark clouds, rain. Brown reeds outside, tossed by the wind. Hangars, a couple of them in ghastly fragments. Then a truck came for us, and we froze to death heading for what turned out to be, for God's sake, a factory!

No kidding, those quote unquote glamorous fly boys live in a factory, and I swear it is colder in here than it is outside. Here is this great black enormous room with a saw-toothed roof. The windows are way the hell up there, and they are all broken. Down here, they have set up a rabbit warren of plywood partitions, some eight feet high, to make individual rooms, *not* for individuals, for each room holds four or five men. Some of the rooms have parachutes spread out for ceilings; ours doesn't. There is a stove in each room, with long stovepipes headed out to the high windows above. The whole place is drafty, smoky, dirty. And cold. In Shep's quarters were his three roommates—in bed, trying to keep warm! There was an extra bed for me (cot, air mattress, sleeping bag), and I got in too—and Shep, after he put more fuel in the tiny potbellied stove. You would never guess what these quote unquote fly boys have scrounged up to use in the stove—hammer handles. Box after box of wooden hammer handles. It is the *essence* of our victory over Japan —this whole goddam dangerous flight—to this!

No, the *real* essence was at chow. Shep has his own jeep; we had to drive to the chow hall. Equally cold, dark, crowded. We lined up for the cafeteria-style line, took trays, waited, looked around: people eating, orange and yellow chrysanthemums on the tables, and suddenly, there I was being served some sort of meat. I looked up—and I sort of jerked my tray back and held it firmly. The guy serving the meat was a Jap! He was dressed in white, neat, shaved head, red face, grinning at me—well, you know, I thought, my God, this is the *enemy*—and I nearly took my damn tray and knocked him over the head. You can't just forgive and forget (can you?). Well, I know it's funny when I write about it, and I only hesitated a few seconds before I let the guy put the meat on my tray, but there we were: I had traveled for three years toward this confrontation, had survived purely by chance, and you can't simply pretend it was all a game, can you? Afterward, back in the factory, everybody sat on boxes around the stove, drinking Japanese beer, and they kidded me about it, about my sense of outrage, but I won't forget it, ever.

.   .   .

Twenty years later, I read and reread the letters. I've edited them a bit here and there, inserting punctuation of sorts, taking out some of the excess underlining; but it is an odd feeling: I can recognize the person who wrote the letters. He isn't much changed, except he has lost some of the enthusiasm, as if nothing any more could shock or surprise him. But has he learned anything?

Some time after the war, I went to a job interview with a much older man, and we got to talking about our military service, and he had been in World War I, and the recall of it took him back into himself. "I was just twenty-one, then, and I was the captain of a gunboat on the Yangtze River. and it was everything that you might imagine it was, and the rest of my life has been an anticlimax."

And this would be true of all of us, to stay perpetually children, if we did not learn anything from our journey to the war.

J—— was an operator. He had connections and offered to take me to buy a kimono, just where he didn't quite say. We drove in his jeep along whole fields of frost-killed cabbages to a nearby village. We turned from a narrow cobblestone street onto a still-narrower, muddy lane and pulled up before an ordinary dwelling. The lane way was absolutely quiet; the sky, the wood house, the ground were a uniform gray except for a spot of bronze chrysanthemums beside the door. We stopped there and removed our muddy shoes, and thus moved into—which century?—but also into the very heartland of the "enemy." (Why had not our fire-bombs destroyed the malignancy of this house? Why did J—— and I not slaughter on the spot everyone we saw?)

"They don't have any English," said J——, "so just smile and bow a little bit at them. This is Grandma." Black kimono, black hair swirled and knotted in the back, a brown face, a mass of wrinkles. "And Grandpa." Thin mustache, unsmiling. "The misses." Blue kimono, ivory-smooth face. "And the kids." Dolls, with runny noses, sucking thumbs, terribly serious. "Papa is conspicuously absent. He die honor-ble death in late war, the son of a bitch."

We all smiled and bowed, and moved to the living room, a square platform around a little fire. Then we all squatted or sat or something (I tried to get my cold feet close to the fire, though I felt no heat from it), and J—— talked a steady stream of chatter. "How'sa kids today, huh? Whyn't you in school, little girl, hey?" But, of course, no one understood anything. Someone got out an English-Japanese language book and puzzled through it trying to comprehend something of his chatter, until J—— said, "Kimonos?" and then, not until then and after he had said it over and over again in a kind of litany, did they understand, and then everyone repeated the word with satisfaction. Grandma made a great search in the language book and came out finally with the word: "Tsoon."

J—— leaned back on his haunches, relieved, and said quietly, "Bastards. They do this every time. They know damn well what I come for. So now we sit. We got to drink the tea. They'll smile and smile, all except Grandpa, and after a long time somebody will come in with the stuff."

We did drink the tea. An iron pot hung on a chain over the barely flickering fire, but the tea was hot and good. After some time, the kimono woman came in, young, cheerful, beautiful, with a package of goods and—but, in short, the kimonos were everyday affairs in dull colors, crepes, no silks—except one, a gorgeous plain scarlet, the sleeves lined in pink. Gradually J—— put in a pile before him my money (twenty dollars) and his goods from the PX: two candy bars, a can of nuts, two bars of soap. Slowly, they made it clear that the only proper exchange would be two cartons of cigarettes, and these we did not have. So after much ceremony, we left, empty-handed.

I think the whole episode vulgar and shameful.

•   •   •

And what was Tokyo like, twenty years ago, under
the Army of Occupation? It was—but how does anyone
know what it was like, and how can one remember, and does
it even matter any more? We drove downtown in Shep's
jeep, through endless surburbs, along with thousands of
bicyclists, Army trucks, charcoal-burning cars, children wav-
ing, traffic policemen who bowed at us; past drug stores with
dried herbs hanging in the windows, a pottery shop with
great red and purple jugs set out by the street, food stores
with queues of women all in kimonos and carrying parasols;
past elegant pine trees and parks, alongside the suburban
train, networks of railroad tracks, past banks and theaters,
stores, crowds of people—and then, suddenly, nothing for
the space of five or ten miles, a blank, a ruin, as far as you
could see, the firebomb area. Not total, for in a great empty
area was a five-story building or a tall chimney beside a pile
of rubble—but a seemingly endless reach of nothing but
broken brick and rusted iron—and it all proceeded up to
a line, a street, and then stopped. There was downtown
Tokyo, seemingly untouched—a city, any city. The destruction marched down to across the street from the emperor's
palace, to the moat (sluggish, lavender), to the small forest
of pine trees and maples (red, yellow), and beyond that were
streetcars and skyscrapers. I could not help comparing half-
destroyed Tokyo with totally destroyed Manila and, vindic-
tive, wishing we had bombed Tokyo with less precision.
Who can know what war is like unless *everything* is destroyed?

In the midst of this, a department store—nightmarish,
crowded with little people in dark clothing, people who
melted away from you as you came close. If you stopped to
examine some pottery or embroidery work, a small crowd
would stop, gather around, stare; when you moved, they fell
away from you. All dark, open, and an organ playing in a
balcony, and the clerk totting up the bill on an abacus.

Then the white masks strapped over faces, and an art exhibit of abstract water colors, and red lacquer bowls and priceless porcelains and dime-store trash—nothing had been touched by the war, and in a fury I would have destroyed it all.

The next day, the overcast began to break, and I went off, with some trepidation, alone, I don't know where. Americans could ride on the suburban trains without paying (so, too, could the Japanese servicemen in uniform), and I simply rode off, away from the city. People scurried on and off the train, too busy to notice me. Out on the platform, doll-sized children juggled bean bags, hoping for a tip (one tiny girl with an infant strapped to her back, its head hung sideways). I got off at a station and wandered until I found a kimono shop, and then, in the back of the store, a scroll painting (the woman, pen in hand, meditating, waiting for words to come). Then back on the train.

At one stop, the dozen or so American servicemen on the train all got off; I wondered why and so abruptly I followed them. Everyone headed in the same direction, though I was too far behind to ask where. The sun broke out of the clouds as if on cue. We were in the country in the late afternoon, and one could just see in the gold of the sun the shape of Fujiyama. We passed (they passed, I followed) a grove of pine trees with graveled paths leading off. We passed under gaudy maple trees; and on cue the wind stirred, and gold paper cascaded about us. We reached at last what looked like some elegant shrine with the tipped-up roof corners, a garden of chrysanthemums, and the air alive with blown leaves. I followed the servicemen in. And inside, a woman at a desk in orange-and-yellow kimono: would I mind waiting a few minutes? Tea, perhaps. And *then* I saw the long line of Army boots and shoes, and the red-cross sign beside the prophylactic station. And I fled this shrine, this whorehouse, laughing at my own stupid naïveté.

I can't forget that. Afterward, at the train station, I sat on a bench and waited for the train back in the direction of Tachikawa—and thought my bitter thoughts for a time. Then some children, five of them, in dark-blue padded clothes, walked past, stopped to stare at me. I found in my pocket the little language book that J—— had given me and looked through it and said to them, "Konnichi wá." They giggled, and then a girl carefully repeated the words, correcting my pronunciation, "Konnichi wa," and so I said it with no accent, the way she did, "Konnichi wa," and added, "Hello" which they repeated. Pretty soon, they were sitting beside me, looking through my book, to say other words to me, and I to them, until the train came, and I had to leave.

RETURN

~~~~~~~~~~~~~~~~~~~~~~~~

I WANTED TO GO BACK HOME. We all
did. Wasn't the war over?

Patriotism was a scarce commodity in the postwar period.
It had never been, to my eyes, very visible, except perhaps in
a few crackpots. I don't mean that we all didn't get a thrill
out of the United States flag; we did, of course, but it was
rather like Pavlov's dog. More motivating in the war was
the sense of a certain work that had to be done; we knew no
more why it had to be done than we knew why we had been
born, but there was the feeling of: Get the job done and
then we can get on to something else; and so we labored and
won the war. The end of the war, however, made any further labor meaningless. So there was great scorn for the
refrigerator-type patriotism so evident in the star-spangled
advertisements in American magazines (the attitude that
we were fighting for the American way of life, for our
Homes, Mothers, and Refrigerators), yet there was also a

RETURN   163

secret urge to have, to get back to, to possess what we had
"won." We saw no reason why we should not, each of us,
return to the States not only immediately, but also before
anyone else.

Even before Hiroshima, the point system of demobilization began to dominate our thinking. I believe the Navy's
first directive on discharge came out August 5, 1945: fifty-
three points were necessary for Naval Reserve officer discharge, based on one point for each year of age and three
points for each year of Navy duty. By that reckoning, I had
thirty-three points and was five years away from discharge.
By the end of August, the war ended, the point system was
revised; but I still had two years to go until discharge. By
October, under the next point system, I could reasonably
expect to be out in one year. The new point system of November—half a point for each year of age, half a point for
every month in the Navy, and a quarter point for every
month overseas—would put me out on exactly May 2, 1946.
A later refinement added twenty-five days' "proceed" time
before discharge, April 7 in my case, provided a relief had
been furnished. That was still eight months after the end
of the war and nearly intolerable, but it was within the
realm of the foreseeable and a base from which to plan my
future. Needless to say, I lived only to accumulate points,
as everyone else, and I grew to hate the whole bloody military system, as did everyone else.

Demobilization of millions of men from all over the
world; administrative "snafu" (situation normal, all fucked
up); congressmen drumming up votes by crying "Bring the
boys home"—it is not surprising that twenty thousand servicemen in the Manila area held an illegal protest meeting
in Rizal Stadium on March 7, 1946. Army or Navy mimeo-
graph machines were used to churn out thousands of sheets
of antimilitary protest. ("Those are as brothers whose
bodies have shared fear, or shared harm, or shared hurt or

indignity.") In short, none of us gave a good goddam about
"winning the peace." We just wanted to go home.

At Mariveles, we did what we could to expedite the demobilization. Our dry dock still belonged to the Army, and
boats assigned to the Army had to have their hulls scraped
of barnacles whether the war ended or no. Nevertheless,
some of our crew had been overseas more than two years,
and in October we were able to ship out some thirty skilled
men. These were replaced in November by twenty-five nonrated (unskilled) seamen, all age nineteen. After these had
been more or less trained, we shipped out thirty-seven men
just before Christmas. They were replaced by ten men.
(Eight of these, incidentally, were named Smith, and one
had no given names at all, just two initials. We could always
get somebody for a job on the dock by yelling out "Smith!")
However, someone ashore goofed up: we got in January
copies of orders for sixty rated men who had been assigned
to us. So we discharged old hands as fast as we could; but
when the new men arrived in February, there were only
twenty-seven of them and they were nonrated (and
with names like Calaiacovo, Manaszkiewicz, and Didome-
nico). The net result was that our skilled crew of one hundred and twenty had been reduced to an unskilled crew of
sixty.

The same shuffle took place among the officers; the force
of three deck officers dropped to two, the Captain and my-
self. I found to my dismay that I was now Executive Officer,
Docking Officer, Maintenance Officer, Commissary Officer,
First Division Officer, Second Division Officer, Education
Officer, Welfare and Recreation Officer, Gunnery Officer,
Diving Officer, Photography Officer, Postal Officer, Public
Relations Officer, and Damage Control Officer. Not only
that, the two warrant officers were replaced by only one new
man. And then the Skipper was replaced, too. Captain
B—— arrived on a Monday, and Captain A—— left early
on Tuesday.

•   •   •

"I never should have relieved him! I never should have let him go! Navy Regs makes it quite clear that a ship must be in good order before a command can be relieved. Why, this is unbelievable!"

"Yes, sir."

"Do you know that when I came on board last night, there was no deck watch?"

"Yes, sir. You see, when the movie is on, the deck watch can't see the screen from the gangway; so it's gotten that he was allowed to move away from there for the movie."

"Not any more, he doesn't! Is that clear?"

"Yes, sir."

"And the man down there now. Do you mean to say he is allowed to stand watch in dungarees?"

"Yes, sir, I guess so, sir."

"You get him into whites, immediately! Whites for the gangway watch, whites for the boat crew, and whites for the liberty party as well."

"Captain, if you don't mind my suggesting it, it's either muddy or dusty in Mariveles; so for the liberty party to wear whites would be, well, ridiculous."

"Whites for the gangway watch, the boat crew, *and* the liberty party. *Is that clear?*"

"Yes, sir."

"Next, I want to know about docking. That tug in there now. When are you going to bring her out?"

"*Me,* sir? Well, sir, it's due to come out tomorrow morning, only I think I should mention that I personally have never docked or undocked anything without making a mess out of it."

"Aren't you the Docking Officer?"

"Yes, sir, but only for two days now. The Executive Officer that left, *he* was the Docking Officer, and we—well, I just was never really trained—my God, can't *you*—"

"I never should have taken command! What *have* you people been doing? When was this deck painted last?"

"Not since I've been here, and that would be eight months and ten days now, sir."

"Isn't that the responsibility of the First Lieutenant? Weren't you the First Lieutenant all that time?"

"Yes, sir, and we tried, sir. The men did start chipping off the rust, but they lost all the chipping hammers overboard, and we've tried every time we went to Manila to get more hammers, but—"

"You mean the men *threw* the hammers overboard so they wouldn't have to work. Didn't Captain A—— do anything about it? Just what did Captain A—— do?"

"If you mean, sir, did he keep a tight ship, well, no, I guess he didn't. After the war ended, you know, and we lost most of our rated men and—"

"Well, Mr. Lee, I want to make it perfectly clear that that was Captain A—— and yesterday, but today I'm in command, and you are the Executive Officer, and that means that you execute *my* orders, and *I* am going to keep a taut ship. *Is* that clear?"

"Yes, sir."

"And one more thing. I'm used to bad coffee in the Navy, but I've never had anything like this."

"Well, sir, the coffee beans we have. They were loaded down into the hold when this dock left the States, and, well, sir, that's been over two years now."

"And *you* are the Commissary Officer?"

"Yes, sir."

"Do you think—oh. *You're* a *Reserve* officer."

"Yes, sir."

"How long have you been overseas?"

"Thirteen months and twenty-two days, sir."

"And when do you expect to be discharged?"

"April 7, sir. Forty-four more days, counting today."

"I never! Never! Ah, well, so be it. We'll have to make do with what we have, Mr. Lee. We'll have to learn to get along with each other."

Captain B—— worked the skin off my ass, and I hated his guts. I used to go over to the Blue Goose and get tight and tell all my troubles to Ida, but even that wasn't very satisfying, for things had changed. Mariveles had become pretty dull. The law of supply and demand worked inexorably, and the price of Black Label Scotch Whiskey of Great Age dropped from ten pesos to seven. The cat houses had multiplied, from two to eight, and the price there dropped from ten pesos to five. Then a Catholic chaplain showed up in the area, insisted that the whole industry be shut down, and after a certain date that any remaining prostitutes be put under arrest. One of our old hands made a valiant, futile attempt to smuggle to Manila on our tug six girls and two pimps. And after that excitement was over, somebody marked out a baseball diamond, which seemed to satisfy the taste of the replacements, so different from that of our veterans.

(Two or three of the girls I had met were now pregnant and without husbands, their men demobilized. I heard of one colored man who paid off his obligation with two hundred and fifty dollars, both parties satisfied.)

Whenever I could get away from Captain B——, I used to go hunting in the hills, either with the new warrant officer or with a carpenter, or alone, but never alone after José Sorreál warned me about pythons. We went after iguana or the wild caribou or wild boars, and this was really exciting. We carried rifles and pistols and hiked in the brown grass savannas past the abandoned rusted trucks, souvenirs of the Battle of Bataan of 1942. It was quite something when an iguana a yard long or more, startled by our approach, would hurry (as fast as a running dog) out of an old fox hole and slither noisily through the dry grass. It was equally great to come across at dusk finally a family of wild boars, completely surprised by our approach, as we were by them, and so there was time enough and we were close enough to see the long curved tusks, yellow, turning brown at the base, before they stampeded off, luckily away from us, not toward us.

And we grew mustaches, those of us on the dock that were old enough, and I have a picture of myself, the sere hills in the background, the rifle over my shoulder, the pistol slung from a web belt, and just the shadow of something under my nose.

We met the Catholic chaplain one day and virtually without introduction launched into an argument about evolution. He was unbelievably fundamentalist, nearly denying that Darwin had ever existed, let alone any validity to his theories. Then abruptly we went with him on his search for a small American cemetery, which he found finally, overgrown with weeds, some of the graves opened and robbed for the sake of the gold fillings in the teeth.

Once, after a long hike, the warrant officer and I found a hot spring bubbling out of the ground with noxious sulfur fumes. A small pond had formed there, so we pulled off our shoes and pants and dangled our legs in the soothing hot water—until a Filipino came by and told us this had been a favorite place for lepers.

Back on board the bastard dock, we chipped that goddam deck to bare metal, burnished it, and put on three fucking coats of paint.

I wanted so desperately to go home. The brown hills of Bataan were not the hills of my home. There, in the spring, tiny white trillium would have fallen like snow.

Suddenly, in March, the Army pulled out of Mariveles. The tents came down one by one, the trucks hauled everything out over the road to San Fernando. Almost overnight there was nothing left in town but the decorated Christmas tree in front of the federal building (the radar "window" for tinsel blowing, glittering in the wind). Suddenly, there were no more boats to dock. We were idle.

Ominously, Captain B—— began to play acey-deucy with me after every meal.

Suddenly, the orders came through: the Army was turning us back to the Navy as of April 1. And suddenly my own discharge orders came through: "When relieved and when directed, on or after April 7 . . . proceed home." But immediately after that came the dock's orders: to depart by tow on or after April 1 for decommissioning in the United States. I did not panic immediately because I knew that the dock could never get ready to leave on time, and in fact secondary orders came through the next day to hold up the dock until a dredge had been taken on board, the dredge to be unloaded at Guam. Then came copies of the orders for my relief, an Ensign F——, presently somewhere in the Philippines, and the Skipper assured me he would let me go the moment my relief came on board—and so we went through a flurry of preparation, the dock to go one way and I the other.

Except, April 7 rolled around and nothing happened. (General Homma was excuted at 0130 on April 3.) Everything was delayed while typhoon winds and rain swept the area. Then promptly on April 10, the dredge arrived to be floated into the dock, brought to Mariveles by the same seagoing tug that would take the dock to Guam and then to the States. I *begged* the Captain to release me without a relief.

"You know I couldn't do that. We're down to half a crew. It's the typhoon season. You can't expect me to do all the work by myself."

He was right, of course. But I *couldn't* wait the week after week after week it would take for the dry dock to be towed back to the States, and so I didn't give up hope.

By noon April 11, the dredge was loaded and everything secured for sea. Suddenly, a radio message from PhilSeaFron —someone to go in to Manila—my relief, of course!—and after hours we located an Army boat that would take me in —four hours one way and no promise that they could get me back (I didn't care!). But when I got to PhilSeaFron at 1800, the man I had to see had, of course, quit for the day. They'd get a message to the dock to hold it, and there was a BOQ where I could spend the night.

On April 12, at 0800, I presented myself to X——.

"Ah, yes. You people all loaded? Ready to go? I called you in because there are some papers here, some inventories that have to be done before decommissioning. Thought you'd have lots of time to work on them underway. A relief? For you? Why, don't be silly, man. I'm overdue for relief myself, and if a live body showed up here, I certainly wouldn't let him get out to you. But you'd better get a move on and get back to the dock."

I think I shouted. I was content enough to miss the fucking departure of the fucking dock, but I knew damn well the Skipper wouldn't shit without me, and what the good goddam was I supposed to use for transportation?

Presently, I was the sole passenger in a Navy crash boat, a PT boat, skimming across Manila Bay at twenty-two knots. The four-hour trip took just one hour and twenty-five minutes—and I said my goodbye to Manila, Corregidor, and Bataan in style and in bitterness. I could have written the sign I'd seen in Manila: "Give it back to the Japs!"

It took us fourteen bloody days to go the sixteen hundred miles to Guam. I saw nothing. We passed Mindoro and Panay and Negros and Bohola and Leyte and came out through the Surigao Straits. We passed over the Mindanao Deep, and the water was purple-black. We passed through storms that held us nearly motionless for hours. The dredge inside the dock weighed four thousand tons, and the wind broadside set up a periodic roll to the dock; a ten-degree roll strained the hundred cleat blocks holding the dredge in place; but we rolled to starboard several times as far as seventeen degrees. We arrived in Guam on April 28—and we calculated that, after we left Guam, it would still take fifty or sixty days to get back to the States. And I was *past* eligible for immediate discharge, my points were up, and I *had* to get home.

And there, in Guam, was my relief, waiting to come on board. I could have kissed him.

"Now, Lee, *think* a moment. Ensign F—— got his commission a month ago. He was *flown* out here. *He has never been on a boat.* Why, he doesn't even know port from starboard. You don't for a moment think that he can handle the red tape of the day-to-day life around here, let alone life at sea, do you, now? Can you conceive of my trying to sleep while that *boy* had the watch? Do I have to remind you that this dock nearly tipped over that night on the way here? Think what that *boy* would do in an emergency. If we had *anybody* on board who had *any* experience *at all*—but you can't honestly ask me to accept that *boy* as your relief."

"Sir, my orders say 'on or after April 7.' It is now April 28. My orders say 'when relieved,' and F—— is my relief."

"Your orders also say 'when directed.' Now, you just get yourself ashore to the personnel office and sit there until they can come up with a *qualified* relief."

So I did just that, for days and days. The dredge was unloaded without my help. Ensign F—— busied himself getting supplies for the long voyage ahead—I wouldn't even talk to him. I sat in the personnel office ashore. I begged, I shouted, I cried, I threatened, I tried bribery, and I got discharges for eighteen more men and eight replacements, but nothing for myself.

On our last afternoon at Guam, I went over to the Officers Club and got drunk.

When I got back to the dock, too late for dinner, to my dazed horror I saw that the Skipper had waited for me in the mess, waited for me to play acey-deucy—and that did it.

"Is that why you're keeping me on board, so you'll have somebody to play acey-deucy with for the next two goddam months? Sir? Honestly, now, isn't it just for your personal convenience that you're keeping me, so I can entertain you?"

Ensign F—— and the warrant officer left the messroom in embarrassment, but I continued.

"You just don't seem to understand the difference between Regular Navy and Naval Reserve, do you? Some people might like this kind of life, but I just want you to know, I loathe it, I really loathe it. I signed up for the duration, sure, but the war has been over so many months I can't count them—and anyway I am legally entitled to my discharge *right now*. I've got to get back before this goddam garbage scow gets back. Look, I'm going back to college. You know the rate we're going I'd never be out in time for the fall semester. Don't you understand? I never did get acclimatized out here and I damn well don't like it. That doesn't matter to you, though, does it? You're just taking it out on me because I'm not Regular Navy and don't want to be, and trying to see just how much shit I'll put up with, and I'm here to tell you, sir! that I've just about had enough!"

Oh, God, I don't want to hear myself any more. For twenty years, I have stood before good, honest Captain B—— and insulted him!

Finally, he could take no more. He ordered me to be silent.

I sat there at the mess table, furious, not quite silent, muttering to myself. After a time, Captain B—— reached behind him and brought out the acey-deucy set. He opened up the board, he sorted out the red and black pieces, he put the dice in the dice cup, rattled them, but did not shake them out; instead, he passed the dice cup to me. I hesitated —and then played.

I beat him five games in a row.

Then we sat there in the dusk (the mess boy too frightened to come in to turn on the lights) and we did not speak, though we lighted cigarette after cigarette.

Outside, over the speaker system, came the movie call: "Screen detail, lay up to the screen. Cobb, Powers, Koval-ski, Cox."

And finally I apologized—which was all he had waited for—and Captain B—— said, "Do you think you can get everything in order to turn over to Ensign F—— before you leave tomorrow?"

May 11, 1946. I am lying on a stretch of wet green grass in front of the Quonset-hut waiting room at the air strip on Kwajalein. Someone's dog was here a minute ago, a large, shaggy, friendly dog, but he has run off into the darkness. The rest of the plane passengers are in the Quonset hut, having yet another cup of coffee. I can see our plane in the hangar; some men on a platform are tinkering with one of the starboard engines.

We nearly took off an hour ago; the plane taxied down to the end of the air strip, the engines revved, and then the plane taxied back again to the hangar. I suppose they will try again in an hour or so. But whether or not we make it up into the sky, whether or not we crash, now strikes me as not very important, since we came so very close to not making it here at all. A person has very little choice in the time of his death, and now I have exhausted my concern. If there was a moment in the past twenty-four hours in which I had a free choice, I cannot remember it. Anyway, we will soon cross the International Date Line, and in a sense it is still twenty-four hours ago. So one could argue that nothing has happened, there was no change, no progress, no movement, no direction, no importance at all. I am back on the dry dock at Guam, forcing the sleepy Ensign F—— all night long to take inventory of the ship's stores.

But I hate death. Now, down at the far end of the air strip, there is a rustling noise, the sound of a rain squall moving toward us (the sound like an iguana in the dry fallen leaves in a bamboo grove). When the rain appears, like a gray curtain, I get up from the grass and run into the hangar and join our plane attendant, who is squatting on his haunches, looking out into the night. The rain pours down.

"You just about didn't make it!" he says cheerfully. I offer him a cigarette and ask about our plane. "Oh, it shouldn't be so long now. They think they got the trouble this time." Then he uses the opportunity to pour out his own anxiety. "Boy, I sure as hell hope they do. I don't wanna go through that again, that sweatin' it out up there with the pilot. Jesus, I don't know how we happened to make it. That navigator we got is sure A-1. Times like this I wisht I'd never been up in the air."

He drags deep on his cigarette and continues: "An' somebody is really gonna get the book thrown at 'em. Nobody heard our emergency call. Nobody here realized that we weren't coming in on the regular channel. And then, by God, nobody saw our emergency flares. The pilot, he had to land that baby without even his wing lights on, and a dark field at that. And that control tower, those guys are dead. They didn't see the flares, and they didn't even see the plane go past them. Nobody knew or cared where we were until we taxied up here."

By the time he finishes talking, the rain has stopped. Steam is rising from the macadam. We had not seen the other plane land, but now it stops in front of the terminal building, and passengers get out. Some of them are women. The plane attendant and I go over to look at them. They seem to be part of a USO troupe. They're almost shapeless in their khakis. Their faces are coated with make-up. One of them has a wilted lei of red flowers, so they are just in from Hawaii and outward bound. Already, men have surrounded them, so I go off and pace back and forth in the darkness.

"I hear you just about didn't make it!" That was what the bartender said at the Officers Club several hours ago. (*Is it really more than twenty years?*) He was an enlisted man, Navy, very busy trying to wash and dry glasses between setting up drinks. It was so late when we got there, we had to eat right away so the kitchen could close—and then drink afterward. We had cold spaghetti and wieners and then went to the bar for highballs. The bar was decorated with pieces of coral, giant sea shells, and the green glass globes from Japanese fishing nets. The bar was crowded. It was a Saturday night, and we discovered there were civilians there too, the forward echelon of the Bikini atom bomb test. There were two hard-looking Navy nurses, hard but elegant in white uniforms. There was one woman in a civilian dress of light blue, escorted by a Navy officer in khakis and cowboy boots.

The bar rapidly became impossibly crowded, so I moved off to the row of slot machines. I had in change just one quarter and put it in the machine and got back fourteen quarters and pocketed them, not willing to push my luck any further.

Because, like a giant bird, a dark bird larger than the plane, death had tagged after us that day—and, accidentally distracted, passed us by. The flight from Guam to Kwajalein took eight hours. At dusk, halfway there, the plane attendant had gone to turn on the stoves that would heat the plates of frozen dinners. Something shorted, the plane's generators went out; all the electricity on the plane went dead. The plane rushed on into the darkness above a sea of clouds barely lit by a new moon. The cabin was in utter darkness, and the cockpit too. The navigator had to use a flashlight to read his charts, but he could not measure the sideways drift of the plane in the invisible wind, although a drift of a half degree would spell life-and-death difference. The pilot used a flashlight to check his dials. The radioman sat before a dead receiver. The navigator looked vainly for the quivering green line of Loran that would "home" the plane. With the emergency gear was a hand-powered radio that could send out SOS signals. This they used. Every land station must listen twice every half hour for signals on the frequency of the emergency radio. But no one heard, no one listened. The plane drifted black through the night, and the navigator took his readings from the stars. Even if there had not been clouds below, there were no landmarks, nothing but the black ocean and the giant bird of death. So only God knows how the navigator located Kwajalein. He must have ordered the plane down through the clouds on mere chance, and in the distance there were the lights.

Then the emergency flare went off with a ping—red and green rockets rushed quickly behind us. The plane banked sharply, circling the little atoll once on what little gasoline was left. The two colors rocketed away from us again. Then the plane seemed to stop in the air as, with wrenching noises, the wheels were let down. We stared out the small round windows, but saw nothing. Ping, the flares went out a third time, and in the mixed colors of light we could distinguish the difference between land and sea, could see the waves on the beach, *right there.* Thud, and again thud, and screech —we were down.

I am still numb with fear. I do care, after all. I want very much to live. We have been on the ready all night long. Now, one rain squall after the other marches down the air strip. I look out, as if I might actually see a hovering black bird. Then, after a while, I can see there is light of sorts in the sky.

Soon, now, the plane will take off. When it climbs up and up and up and reaches the sun—a gold caught all over the plane and shining in the propellers—then I will be free.

1968

~~~~~~~~~~~~~~~

MORE THAN TWENTY YEARS have passed.
I remember, as an undergraduate, hearing some lecturer
tell us that perpetual peace was impossible, that we had to
acknowledge the existence of world wars and be content
with, at the most, twenty years of peace between wars. Those
twenty years, more than twenty years, have now passed, as
if of no more duration than that night I spent in May of
1946, waiting for the plane at Kwajalein.

Since then, my home town in Iowa has dwindled in size.
The little train on which I left on my way to the war stopped
running years ago, and now there is not even bus service to
my town. In the interval, my father died. To pay his debts
we had to sell the farm he had inherited from his father,
and the pasture where the trillium used to bloom has been
plowed into cornfields. But the money left over financed my
six years of graduate education, or half of it, after I had used
up the money from the GI Bill. So there was never any
question about staying in Iowa, since I had the money to

leave. And it had been a simple decision, after seeing the destruction in Manila, to give up my career in architecture. (Why rebuild what could so easily be destroyed?)

Therefore I lived in a tenement house in Chicago and, among other things, studied cultural history at the University of Chicago. In that medieval place I met Professor Arnold Bergstraesser, a fabulous man. He had been a German soldier in World War I, and an American hand grenade had exploded in his face. One side of his face was grotesquely mangled, and the other side was left clear. When he lectured, he paced back and forth in front of the class. He lectured an hour and a half at a time, without notes, on Hegel, Spengler, Marx—a marvelous, exciting parade of learning.

In his office once I blurted out that, end of the war or no, I still hated the Germans. "Ach," said Bergstraesser, "so do I, in a way. But here, take this book; read it; tell me what you think of it." It was Konrad Heiden's *Der Fuehrer,* and a week later I went back to Bergstraesser and said, in effect: "In the last free election in Germany, May 5, 1933, forty-three and nine tenths per cent of the Germans voted for Hitler. There was a free press; it was by then perfectly clear that Hitler would be a dictator. They voted freely and openly for him. Tell me, please, why did the Germans want Hitler?"

Bergstraesser slowly removed the cigarette from his mouth and turned full face to me and said hoarsely, tragically, *"I don't know!"*

You understand from this my own sense of saintliness— it was the Germans, the Japanese, who were bad, not I. If a man like the late Professor Bergstraesser in a lifetime of study had no certain answer on the complexity of the causes of war, having "fought," where was *my* further obligation? Anyway, we were at peace. I became engaged to the girl who sat next to me in a class, and in no time my graduate learning had to be considered in terms of a marketable commodity. I became a teacher, and thus the time passed.

Some four years ago, I took my sons back to Iowa so they could see in the city park the log cabin where their great-grandfather had taught school, and see the tombstone of their grandfather, and walk the wooded hills of my own youth. We visited an uncle, who let us go hunting in the orchard behind his farmhouse. I had inherited from my father a .22 rifle, and although my sons had shot at targets before that October morning, they had not shot at live game. They were thirteen and eight years old. At the far end of the old apple orchard were some pine trees, and these were filled with squirrels. In no time, each of the boys had shot a squirrel (my major concern, in the excitement, to see that they did not shoot me). My uncle cut off the tails and the paws of the two dead squirrels and gave them to the boys.

Later, like the heat of the sun on the back of my neck, like a blow, I realized what I had done, what I had taught my boys. I was no pacifist. Like the Germans, I had enjoyed the war.

War is all right, you see, if you accept the idea of the domination of death. Then it does not matter if you, as an individual, are killed in a war or are to die later, in the peace. The war is within you, in every man, and no one is responsible individually for anything.

There are only moments, like the night at Kwajalein. I don't know what it was—neither revelation nor understanding, and hardly even awareness, for the awareness was partial, and it did not come for more than twenty years. But there was something.

And so, as if it were yesterday, the plane took off from Kwajalein at dawn, and there was no more mechanical trouble. We flew to Honolulu and to San Francisco, and then I took the train to Chicago for demobilization, and then went home for a while. My mother had saved all my letters. Without looking at them, I wrapped the whole bundle in brown paper, and only recently, in the anguish of peace, took them down to read again.

A NOTE

ABOUT THE AUTHOR

ROBERT EDSON LEE was born in Sac City, Iowa, in
1921 and was raised in Nebraska. He was graduated from
Iowa State College in 1943 in architectural engineering
and received the Ph.D. in American Studies from the
State University of Iowa in 1957. He has taught at Vas-
sar College, at the State University of Iowa, and since
1957 at the University of Colorado, where he is now professor of American literature and director of the Colorado Scholars program. During 1967–8 he has been
visiting Fulbright lecturer in American literature at the
University of Warsaw. Mr. Lee is the author of *From
West to East: Studies in the Literature of the American
West* (1966). He is married and the father of two sons.

A NOTE

ON THE TYPE

THE TEXT of this book was set on the Linotype in Baskerville. Linotype Baskerville is a facsimile cutting from type cast from the original matrices of a face designed by John Baskerville. The original face was the forerunner of the "modern" group of type faces.

John Baskerville (1706–75), of Birmingham, England, a writing-master, with a special renown for cutting inscriptions in stone, began experimenting about 1750 with punch-cutting and making typographical material. It was not until 1757 that he published his first work. His types, at first criticized, in time were recognized as both distinct and elegant, and his types as well as his printing were greatly admired.

Composed by The Book Press Incorporated, Brattleboro, Vermont, printed by Halliday Lithograph, West Hanover, Massachusetts, and bound by Halliday Lithograph, West Hanover, Massachusetts.

Typography and binding design by Kenneth Miyamoto.